Implementing Investigations in Grade 1

Spiral to Infinity Steve Allen

"Fractal images are often made up of small images-within-images, constantly repeating and going smaller and smaller."– **Steve Allen**

Investigations

IN NUMBER, DATA, AND SPACE®

Power Polygons™ is a trademark of ETA/Cuisenaire®.

Use of the trademark or company name implies no relationship, sponsorship, endorsement, sale, or promotion on the part of Pearson Education, Inc., or its affiliates.

Glenview, Illinois • Boston, Massachusetts
Chandler, Arizona • Upper Saddle River, New Jersey

The Investigations Curriculum was developed by TERC, Cambridge, MA.

This material is based on work supported by the National Science Foundation ("NSF") under Grant No. ESI-0095450. Any opinions, findings, and conclusions or recommendations expressed in this material are those of the author(s) and do not necessarily reflect the views of the National Science Foundation.

ISBN-13: 978-0-328-60215-5

ISBN-10: 0-328-60215-9

2 3 4 5 6 7 8 9 10 V063 14 13 12 11

Co-Principal Investigators

Susan Jo Russell

Karen Economopoulos

TERC

Authors

Lucy Wittenberg
Director Grades 3–5

Karen Economopoulos
Director Grades K–2

Virginia Bastable
(SummerMath for Teachers,
Mt. Holyoke College)

Katie Hickey Bloomfield

Keith Cochran

Darrell Earnest

Arusha Hollister

Nancy Horowitz

Erin Leidl

Megan Murray

Young Oh

Beth W. Perry

Susan Jo Russell

Deborah Schifter
(Education
Development Center)

Kathy Sillman

Note: Unless otherwise noted, all contributors listed above were staff of the Education Research Collaborative at TERC during their work on the curriculum. Other affiliations during the time of development are listed.

Administrative Staff

Amy Taber
Project Manager

Beth Bergeron

Lorraine Brooks

Emi Fujiwara

Contributing Authors

Denise Baumann

Jennifer DiBrienza

Hollee Freeman

Paula Hooper

Jan Mokros

Stephen Monk
(University of Washington)

Mary Beth O'Connor

Judy Storeygard

Cornelia Tierney

Elizabeth Van Cleef

Carol Wright

Technology

Jim Hammerman

Classroom Field Work

Amy Appell

Rachel E. Davis

Traci Higgins

Julia Thompson

Collaborating Teachers

This group of dedicated teachers carried out extensive field testing in their classrooms, met regularly to discuss issues of teaching and learning mathematics, provided feedback to staff, welcomed staff into their classrooms to document students' work, and contributed both suggestions and written material that has been incorporated into the curriculum.

Bethany Altchek

Linda Amaral

Kimberly Beauregard

Barbara Bernard

Nancy Buell

Rose Christiansen

Chris Colbath-Hess

Lisette Colon

Kim Cook

Frances Cooper

Kathleen Drew

Rebeka Eston Salemi

Thomas Fisher

Michael Flynn

Holly Ghazey

Susan Gillis

Danielle Harrington

Elaine Herzog

Francine Hiller

Kirsten Lee Howard

Liliana Klass

Leslie Kramer

Melissa Lee Andrichak

Kelley Lee Sadowski

Jennifer Levitan

Mary Lou LoVecchio

Kristen McEnaney

Maura McGrail

Kathe Millett

Florence Molyneaux

Amy Monkiewicz

Elizabeth Monopoli

Carol Murray

Robyn Musser

Christine Norrman

Deborah O'Brien

Timothy O'Connor

Anne Marie O'Reilly

Mark Paige

Margaret Riddle

Karen Schweitzer

Elisabeth Seyferth

Susan Smith

Debra Sorvillo

Shoshanah Starr

Janice Szymaszek

Karen Tobin

JoAnn Trauschke

Ana Vaisenstein

Yvonne Watson

Michelle Woods

Mary Wright

Advisors

Deborah Lowenberg Ball,
University of Michigan

Hyman Bass, Professor of Mathematics and Mathematics Education
University of Michigan

Mary Canner, Principal, Natick Public Schools

Thomas Carpenter, Professor of Curriculum and Instruction,
University of Wisconsin-Madison

Janis Freckmann, Elementary Mathematics Coordinator,
Milwaukee Public Schools

Lynne Godfrey, Mathematics Coach,
Cambridge Public Schools

Ginger Hanlon, Instructional Specialist in Mathematics,
New York City Public Schools

DeAnn Huinker, Director, Center for Mathematics and
Science Education Research, University of Wisconsin-Milwaukee

James Kaput, Professor of Mathematics, University of
Massachusetts-Dartmouth

Kate Kline, Associate Professor, Department of Mathematics
and Statistics, Western Michigan University

Jim Lewis, Professor of Mathematics,
University of Nebraska-Lincoln

William McCallum, Professor of Mathematics,
University of Arizona

Harriet Pollatsek, Professor of Mathematics,
Mount Holyoke College

Debra Shein-Gerson, Elementary Mathematics Specialist,
Weston Public Schools

Gary Shevell, Assistant Principal,
New York City Public Schools

Liz Sweeney, Elementary Math Department,
Boston Public Schools

Lucy West, Consultant, Metamorphosis:
Teaching Learning Communities, Inc.

This revision of the curriculum was built on the work of the many authors who contributed to the first edition (published between 1994 and 1998). We acknowledge the critical contributions of these authors in developing the content and pedagogy of *Investigations*:

Authors

Joan Akers

Michael T. Battista

Douglas H. Clements

Karen Economopoulos

Marlene Kliman

Jan Mokros

Megan Murray

Ricardo Nemirovsky

Andee Rubin

Susan Jo Russell

Cornelia Tierney

Contributing Authors

Mary Berle-Carman

Rebecca B. Corwin

Rebeka Eston

Claryce Evans

Anne Goodrow

Cliff Konold

Chris Mainhart

Sue McMillen

Jerrie Moffet

Tracy Noble

Kim O'Neil

Mark Ogonowski

Julie Sarama

Amy Shulman Weinberg

Margie Singer

Virginia Woolley

Tracey Wright

Contents

Contents

PART 1

Collaborating with the Authors

Goals and Guiding Principles

Investigations in Number, Data, and Space is a K–5 mathematics curriculum designed to engage students in making sense of mathematical ideas. Six major goals guided the development of this curriculum. The curriculum is designed to

- Support students to make sense of mathematics and learn that they can be mathematical thinkers.

- Focus on computational fluency with whole numbers as a major goal of the elementary grades.

- Provide substantive work in important areas of mathematics—rational numbers, geometry, measurement, data, and early algebra—and connections among them.

- Emphasize reasoning about mathematical ideas.

- Communicate mathematics content and pedagogy to teachers.

- Engage the range of learners in understanding mathematics.

Underlying these goals are three guiding principles that are touchstones for the *Investigations* team as we approach both students and teachers as agents of their own learning:

1. *Students have mathematical ideas.* Students come to school with ideas about numbers, shapes, measurements, patterns, and data. If given the opportunity to learn in an environment that stresses making sense of mathematics, students build on the ideas they already have and learn about new mathematics they have never encountered. They learn mathematical content and develop fluency and skill that is well grounded in meaning. Students learn that they are capable of having mathematical ideas, applying what they know to new situations, and thinking and reasoning about unfamiliar problems.

2. *Teachers are engaged in ongoing learning* about mathematics content, pedagogy, and student learning. The curriculum provides material for professional development, to be used by teachers individually or in groups, that supports teachers' continued learning as they use the curriculum over several years. The *Investigations* curriculum materials are designed as much to be a dialogue with teachers as to be a core of content for students.

3. *Teachers collaborate with the students and curriculum materials* to create the curriculum as enacted in the classroom. The only way for a good curriculum to be used well is for teachers to be active participants in implementing it. Teachers use the curriculum to maintain a clear, focused, and coherent agenda for mathematics teaching. At the same time, they observe and listen carefully to students, try to understand how they are thinking, and make teaching decisions based on these observations.

The Teacher-Student-Curriculum Partnership

Mathematics teaching and learning at its best is a collaboration among teachers, students, and the curriculum. Both the teacher and the curriculum contribute to this partnership in important ways. The curriculum materials provide a coherent, carefully sequenced core of mathematics content for students and supportive professional development material for teachers. Teachers are active partners in learning the curriculum well, understanding how each mathematical focus is developed, and implementing the curriculum in a way that accommodates the needs of their particular students.

The *Investigations* curriculum was field-tested in many different classrooms, representing a range of students and teachers, over several years. Thousands of hours of classroom observation, documentation, analysis of student work, and meetings with teachers were involved. Activities and the way they are presented to students were revised again and again.

Each time a curriculum unit was tested in a classroom, no matter how many times it had been tried and revised before, there was always more to discover about how students learn and how activities can be revised and modified to support them. This process, we have come to believe, can be endless. Just as you, a classroom teacher, learn more about students' learning each year, so do those of us who develop the curriculum. At some point we decide that, considering all the evidence, the curriculum has been sufficiently tested and works well for a wide range of students.

This lengthy and detailed process has resulted in a coherent core curriculum that is based on the real needs of real students and teachers. The process has also provided ample evidence that the collaboration of the teacher is essential. Only the teacher can understand and support the particular learning needs of a particular class of students in a particular school year. Only the teacher is present every day in the classroom, observing students' work, listening to their discourse, and developing an understanding of their mathematical ideas by analyzing what they say and do. In mathematics, as in any subject, only the teacher can continually assess students' strengths and needs and think through how best to accommodate differences to involve all students in substantive and challenging work.

How *Investigations* Supports the Teacher's Role

Modifying the curriculum and making it work in your classroom requires knowing the curriculum well. It means taking the time to understand the mathematics focus of each lesson and how the mathematical ideas build over many lessons. Learning the curriculum well means holding back the urge to change activities because you think they are too easy or too difficult for your students before you have tried them and actually seen your students' work. Keep in mind that the way ideas are developed and sequenced has been researched and tested in multiple classrooms, and many suggestions for accommodations are already built into the

curriculum. Teachers tell us that they generally follow the curriculum as it is written the first year, and that they learn a great deal when activities that they thought would not work with their students turn out to be crucial to student learning.

You are an active partner in this teacher-student-curriculum partnership, and the curriculum must support your complex job by providing information about mathematics content and student learning. From the beginning, our intention in developing *Investigations* has been to create a professional development tool for teachers—a tool that provides opportunities for learning about mathematics content, how students learn, and effective pedagogy. Our design focuses as much on the teacher as learner as on the student as learner.

Two sections at the beginning of each curriculum unit, Mathematics in This Unit and Assessment in This Unit, provide an overview of the mathematics content, Math Focus Points, and benchmarks for student learning. The Math Focus Points for each session and the assessment benchmarks tell the mathematical story line of each curriculum unit so that you can productively guide students' work. Math Focus Points make explicit the purposes of the activities in each session and help you make choices about how to guide discussions. The assessment benchmarks for each curriculum unit are an aid in determining priorities and interpreting students' work.

The "teacher talk" printed in blue in each session is also an aid for focusing an activity and choosing questions to ask. It is not a script for how to address your students; it is a guide based on classroom experience with different ways of talking about mathematical ideas, introducing activities, and asking effective questions.

Teacher Notes collected at the end of each curriculum unit focus on key mathematical ideas and how students learn them. Because having students reason about, articulate, and justify their ideas is such a central part of the curriculum, Dialogue Boxes provide examples of student discussion and teachers' efforts to focus this discussion. Additionally, examples of what students might say in class appear within the session descriptions.

To further support your work with the curriculum, this *Implementing Investigations in Grade 1* book provides an overview of the math content for the entire year (Part 3), a set of Teacher Notes that applies to the curriculum as a whole (Part 6), and a set of classroom cases written by teachers that provides examples of how they work with the range of learners in their classrooms (Part 7).

Teachers who use the *Investigations* curriculum over several years find that, as they teach a curriculum unit more than once, they gradually read more and more of the supporting material and incorporate it into their work with students. Teachers also use features such as the Teacher Notes and Dialogue Boxes as part of grade-level study groups or within other professional development structures. The better you know the curriculum and your students, the more you can internalize the mathematics focus and sequence and the better decisions you can make to support your students' learning.

PART 2

Using *Investigations*

Components of the Program

Curriculum Units

The curriculum at each grade level is organized into nine units (seven for kindergarten). These curriculum units are your teaching guides for the program. The unit organization is further described in the next section, "Using the Curriculum Units."

Each curriculum unit in Grade 1 offers from 2 to 5 weeks of work and focuses on the area of mathematics identified in the unit's subtitle.

This pacing is based on a school year that starts in early September, ends in late June, and has vacation weeks in February and April. The pacing will vary according to school calendars but may also vary depending on the needs of students, the school's years of experience with this curriculum, and other local factors.

Grade 1 Curriculum Units

Unit	Title	Number of Sessions	Suggested Pacing
1	**How Many of Each?** Addition, Subtraction, and the Number System 1	25	September– mid-October
2	**Making Shapes and Designing Quilts** 2-D Geometry	16	mid-October– early November
3	**Solving Story Problems** Addition, Subtraction, and the Number System 2	25	mid-November– December
4	**What Would You Rather Be?** Data Analysis	13	January
5	**Fish Lengths and Animal Jumps** Measurement	11	February
6	**Number Games and Crayon Puzzles** Addition, Subtraction, and the Number System 3	20	March
7	**Color, Shape, and Number Patterns** Patterns and Functions	15	April
8	**Twos, Fives, and Tens** Addition, Subtraction, and the Number System 4	18	May
9	**Blocks and Boxes** 3-D Geometry	16	June

The curriculum units are designed for use in the sequence shown. Each succeeding unit builds on the previous unit, both within and across strands. For example, the four units that focus on addition and subtraction (Units 1, 3, 6, and 8) develop a sequence of ideas across the four units. These ideas are built on throughout the first-grade curriculum, for example, as students figure out the total number of pattern blocks used in a design in Unit 2 (2-D Geometry), as they write equations that represent their data in Unit 4 (Data Analysis), and as they solve comparison problems in Unit 5 (Measurement).

Resource Masters and Transparencies

Each Resource Masters and Transparencies CD contains the reproducible materials needed for classroom instruction. The use of all these materials for particular Investigations is specified in the curriculum units.

Investigations Software

Shapes Software for Grade 1 provides an environment in which students investigate a variety of geometric ideas, including relationships between shapes; how shapes combine to make other shapes; symmetry; and geometric transformations such as rotations (turns), translations (slides), and reflections (flips). This software is provided as a disk to be used with Unit 2, *Making Shapes, Designing Quilts,* and is also available through the Pearson website.

Investigations for the Interactive Whiteboard

Each grade has whole-class instructional support that enhances the session's content as well as the daily Classroom Routines.

Differentiation and Intervention Handbook

Differentiation activities are included for each Investigation along with a quiz that can be used after an Investigation is completed.

Student Activity Book

A booklet accompanying each curriculum unit contains the consumable pages for student work, including in-class work, game recording sheets, and all pages for daily practice and for homework. The *Student Activity Book* is also available as a single volume, with all the curriculum units in one book.

Student Math Handbook

A single handbook for each grade level in Grades 1–5 offers a valuable reference to the math words and ideas introduced in the curriculum units, as well as instruction pages for playing all the games. This book is designed to be used flexibly: as a resource for students during class work, as a book students can take home for reference while doing homework and playing math games with their families, and/or as a reference for families to better understand the work their children are doing in class.

Manipulatives Kit

A kit of materials is coordinated with the activities and games at each grade level. The Grade 1 kit includes class sets of the following items:

Buttons

Monthly pocket calendar with removable numbers

Demonstration clock

Coin sets (pennies, nickels, dimes, quarters, half dollars, dollars)

Connecting cubes

Color tiles

Two-color counters

Craft sticks

Blank cubes and labels

1–6 dot cubes

Geoboards and rubber bands

Geoblocks

Hundreds board set

Pocket 100 chart with extra numbers and pattern markers

1–6 number cubes

Class number line

Pattern blocks

Power Polygons™

Shells

Overhead tools: color tiles, pattern blocks, coins

Cards in Card Kit

Manufactured cards are used with some of the activities and games at each grade level. The cards for Grade 1 are as follows:

Primary Number Cards

Dot Addition Cards

Squares: Singles, Pairs, and Fives

Fish Sets 1, 2, and 3

Baby and Basketball Player Steps

Implementing *Investigations* in Grade 1

At each grade level, this guide to implementing *Investigations* includes an overview of the curriculum; suggestions for using the curriculum units in your classroom; a closer look at the mathematics content of that particular grade, including lists of the Math Focus Points for each curriculum unit; program-wide Teacher Notes that explain some key ideas underlying the curriculum; and a set of case studies about working with a range of learners that can be used for professional development.

The Curriculum Units

The curriculum unit is your main teaching tool. It is your blueprint for the sequence and purpose of the daily lessons; it also contains guidelines for assessment, suggestions for differentiating instruction, and professional development materials to support your teaching.

Structure of a Curriculum Unit

Each curriculum unit is divided into Investigations. An Investigation focuses on a set of related mathematical ideas, coordinating students' work in hands-on activities, written activities, and class discussions over a period of several days.

Investigations are divided into one-hour *sessions,* or lessons. Sessions include the following features:

- *Math Focus Points:* This list of what students will be doing mathematically highlights the goals of each session.

- *Activities:* A session contains from one to three activities, organized as work for the whole class, small groups, pairs, or individuals.

- *Discussion:* Many sessions include whole-class time during which students compare methods and results and share conclusions. A subset of the session's Focus Points helps you guide each discussion.

- *Math Workshop:* In some sessions, students work in a Math Workshop format. Individually, in pairs, or in groups, they choose from and cycle through a set of related activities. This setup is further discussed in a later section, "All About Math Workshop" (pp. 12–14).

- *Assessment:* Students are assessed through both written activities and observations; see "Assessment in This Unit" for further information.

- *Session Follow-up:* Homework is provided once a week at Grade 1. In addition, each session includes a page for Daily Practice. These pages offer either ongoing review of materials from previous curriculum units or directed practice of content in the current curriculum unit. They can be used either for additional homework or for in-class practice. Relevant pages in the *Student Math Handbook* are also referenced here.

Your Math Day

The *Investigations* curriculum assumes that you spend 1 hour of each classroom day on mathematics, in addition to conducting brief Classroom Routines (further described later in this section and in Part 4 of this book). A chart called Today's Plan appears at the beginning of each session, laying out the suggested pacing for the activities in that 1-hour session. While you may need to adapt this structure to your particular classroom needs, be aware that it is important to move through all the activities because they are carefully designed to offer continued work on the key mathematical ideas. It is also essential that you allow time for class discussions, where students have an opportunity to articulate their own ideas, compare solutions, and consolidate understanding. See Teacher Note: Discussing Mathematical Ideas, on pages 62–64, for further information on the importance of these class discussions.

Differentiated Instruction

Within the sessions, you will regularly see a feature titled "Differentiation: Supporting the Range of Learners." This feature offers ideas for intervention or extensions related to the particular work of that session. Ideas for helping English Language Learners are offered at the beginning of the curriculum unit and where applicable in the sessions. In addition, Part 7 of this book, "Working with the Range of Learners" presents situations from actual *Investigations* classrooms and invites you to consider how these case studies can inform your own teaching practice.

Classroom Routines

These brief activities, described in a box below Today's Plan for each session, require about 10 minutes of additional daily work outside of math time. These routines, an important part of the *Investigations* curriculum, offer ongoing skill building, practice, and review that support the regular math work. They also reinforce the work students have done in previous curriculum units and help students increase their repertoire of strategies for mental calculation and problem solving. Part 4 of this book, "Classroom Routines," provides detailed explanations of the activities to plan for Grade 1.

Assessment in This Curriculum Unit

Opportunities for assessment are carefully woven throughout the curriculum units. A section at the beginning of each curriculum unit identifies the benchmarks students will be expected to meet and specifies key activities you can observe, as well as the particular assessment activities where students will produce written work for your review. The final session in each curriculum unit is devoted to the End-of-Unit Assessment. Each written assessment in the curriculum unit is accompanied by a Teacher Note that provides examples of student work and guidelines that help you assess whether your students are meeting the benchmarks. For observed assessments, an assessment checklist is provided; here you can record notes about what students understand as you observe them engaged in the session's activities.

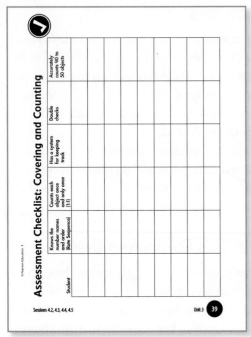

▲ An example of an Assessment Checklist

"Ongoing Assessment: Observing the Students at Work" is a regular feature of the sessions. It identifies the particular math focus and lists questions for you to consider as you observe your students solving problems, playing math games, and working on activities. Teacher observations are an important part of ongoing assessment. Although individual observations may be little more than snapshots of a student's experience with a single activity, when considered together over time, they can provide an informative and detailed picture. These observations can be useful in documenting and assessing a student's growth and offer important sources of information when preparing for family conferences or writing student reports.

You may want to develop a system to record and keep track of your observations of students. The most important aspect of a record-keeping system is that it be both manageable and useful for you. Some teachers use systems such as the following:

- Jot down observations of students' work on a class list of names. Because the space is somewhat limited, it is not possible to write lengthy notes; however, when kept over time, these short observations provide important information.

- Place stick-on address labels on a clipboard. Take notes on individual students and then peel these labels off and put them in a file for each student.

- Jot down brief notes at the end of each week. Some teachers find that this is a useful way of reflecting on the class as a whole, on the curriculum, and on individual students. Planning for the next week's activities can benefit from these weekly reflections.

Observation checklists, student work on written assessments, and other examples of students' written work can be collected in a portfolio. Suggestions for particular work that might be saved in a portfolio are listed at the beginning of each curriculum unit, under "Assessment in This Unit."

Professional Development

One guiding principle of the *Investigations* curriculum is to provide support that helps teachers improve their own understanding of the mathematics that they are teaching and the learning that they observe in their students. To this end, the following materials are included in the curriculum for teachers' professional development:

- *Mathematics in This Unit:* An essay at the beginning of each curriculum unit explains in detail the Mathematical Emphases of the unit, the Math Focus Points related to each area of emphasis, and the work students will be doing in each area.

- *Algebra Connections in This Unit:* This essay, appearing in each of the number and operations units and in the patterns, functions, and change units, explains how the activities and ideas of the curriculum unit are laying a foundation for students' later work with algebra.

- *Math Notes, Teaching Notes, and Algebra Notes:* Found in the margins of the sessions, these brief notes provide information about mathematics content or student thinking, as well as teaching tips to help teachers better understand the work of that session.

- *Teacher Notes:* These essays, collected at the end of each curriculum unit, provide further practical information about the mathematics content and how students learn it. Many of the notes were written in response to questions from teachers or to discuss important issues that arose in field-test classrooms. They offer teachers help with thinking about mathematical ideas that may be unfamiliar to them; they also provide guidance for observing and assessing students' work.

- *Dialogue Boxes:* Also at the end of each curriculum unit are Dialogue Boxes that reflect classroom scenarios related to the activities of the unit. Since these Dialogue Boxes are based on actual teacher-student interactions, you learn how students typically express their mathematical ideas, what issues and confusions arise in their thinking, and how some teachers have chosen to guide particular class discussions.

Working with Families

Families are important partners with schools in the process of teaching mathematics. Because the teaching of mathematics has been evolving, many families may be unfamiliar with the approaches taken by the *Investigations* curriculum. For this reason, a number of Family Letters are provided. In Grade 1, these letters include the following:

- The first Family Letter in each curriculum unit, About the Mathematics in This Unit, introduces families to the mathematics that their children will be doing and to the benchmarks for that unit.

- A second letter in each curriculum unit, Related Activities to Try at Home, is sent home sometime after the first. It suggests related activities that families can do together and children's books that support students' work in mathematics.

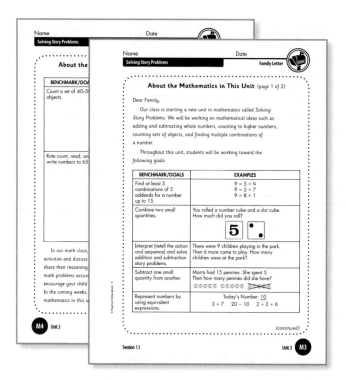

▲ An example of a Family Letter

- An additional letter provided in the first curriculum unit of the year, About Mathematics Homework, gives suggestions for helping students with their homework by establishing a regular time for homework, setting up a good working environment, providing basic materials, and asking productive questions.

The Student Math Handbook is another valuable tool for working with families. The Math Words and Ideas section of this book provides an overview of the year's mathematics work, a closer look at the ideas and the kinds of problems students encounter, examples of student solutions, and questions that families and students can talk about together. The Handbook also contains game directions for use at school or home.

Setting Up the *Investigations* Classroom

As you begin using the *Investigations* curriculum, you may find yourself making decisions about how to set up the tables and chairs in your classroom and where to keep your materials. Students will at various times need to work individually, in pairs or small groups, and as a whole class. When working in pairs or small groups, they need to be able to see one another's work and listen to one another's ideas. Bringing students together for whole-group discussion is also a regular feature of the curriculum, and during these discussions it is important that students can easily see and hear one another. Ways of making this work are further discussed in the Teacher Note: Discussing Mathematical Ideas, on pages 62–64. You must also find ways to make materials and games easily accessible and consider how to organize the room for Math Workshops.

Materials as Tools for Learning

Tools and materials are used throughout the *Investigations* curriculum. Students of all ages benefit from being able to use materials to model and solve problems and explain their thinking. Encourage all students to use tools and materials and to explain how they use them. If materials are used only when someone is having difficulty, students can get the mistaken idea that using materials is a less sophisticated and less valued way of solving a problem or modeling a solution. Therefore, they should see how different people, including the teacher, use a variety of materials to solve the same problem.

Get to Know the Materials Familiarize yourself with some of the main materials students will use. In Grade 1 these include connecting cubes, pattern blocks, Geoblocks, Power Polygons, and Geoboards. In some units there are Teacher Notes that describe particular materials in detail. For example, these might provide the names and mathematical definitions of the shapes in a given set, illustrations of each shape, and information about how to talk about them with students.

Storing Materials Many of the *Investigations* materials come in large containers. Split these sets into smaller, equivalent subsets and store each in a clear container or shoe box, labeled with the name and a picture of the material. Include a small cup to use as a scoop. Store materials where they are easily accessible to students, perhaps on a bookshelf or along a windowsill. In addition to pattern blocks, Geoblocks, and connecting cubes, items such as coins, 100 charts, and paper (blank and grid) are important mathematical tools that should be available to students. Individual units also provide suggestions on preparing some materials for classroom use.

Introducing a New Material Students need time to explore a new material before using it in structured activities. By freely exploring a material, students will discover many of its important characteristics and will have some understanding of when it might make sense to use it. Although some free exploration is built into regular math time, many teachers make materials available to students during free time or before or after school.

Plan How Students Will Use Materials The more available materials are, the more likely students are to use them. Having materials available means that they are readily accessible and that students are allowed to make decisions about which tools to use, and when and how to use them. In much the same way that you choose the best tool to use for certain projects or tasks, students also should be encouraged to think about which material best meets their needs. Initially you may need to place materials close to students as they work. Gradually students should be expected to decide what they need and get materials on their own.

In order to make such a system work, you will need to establish clear expectations about how materials will be used and cared for.

- **Sharing Materials.** Even though a scoop should guarantee an ample assortment and quantity of materials, students might not get the exact piece they desire. Conversations about sharing are critical.

- **Using Materials Appropriately.** Rules and policies for the appropriate use of materials should be established at the beginning of the year. This might include things such as not throwing the materials, not drawing on them, and so on. Consider asking the students to suggest rules for how materials should and should not be used. Students are often more attentive to rules and policies that they have helped create.

- **Cleaning Up Materials.** Making an announcement a few minutes before the end of a work time helps prepare students for the transition that is about to occur. You can then give students several minutes to return materials to their containers and shelves and to double-check the floor for any stray materials.

Games in the *Investigations* Curriculum

The games included in this curriculum are a central part of the mathematics in each curriculum unit, not just an enrichment activity. Games are used to develop concepts and to practice skills, such as counting and comparing quantities, sorting and classifying, adding and subtracting small amounts, or finding combinations of a given number. The rationale for using games is as follows:

- Games provide engaging opportunities for students to deepen their understanding of numbers and operations and to practice computation.

- Playing games encourages strategic mathematical thinking as students find an optimal way (rather than just any way) of "winning" the game.

- Games provide repeated practice without requiring the teacher to provide new problems.

- While students are playing the games, the teacher is free to observe students or to work with individuals or small groups.

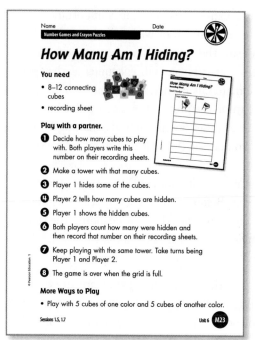

▲ An example of game instructions

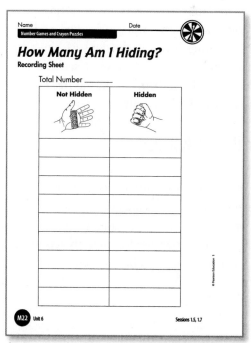

▲ An example of a game recording sheet

Before introducing a game to students, it is important that you play the game yourself or with colleagues. By doing so you will learn the rules of the game, explore the mathematical ideas that students will encounter as they play, and figure out the materials needed for the game. This will also help you determine the preparation needed (for instance, cutting out cards, gathering other materials, making "game packs") and helps you decide the best way to introduce the game to your students (pre-teaching it to some students, small or whole group introduction, etc.). For some games, variations are offered. Before using these variations, or any others you might think of, consider how changing the rules of the game changes the mathematical ideas with which students are working.

Because students find them engaging, games are an excellent vehicle for providing repeated practice, without the need for the teacher to provide new problems. Therefore, students play games repeatedly, over time, throughout the *Investigations* curriculum. The more students play, the better. Therefore, some teachers encourage students to play games at other times as well: in the morning as students arrive, during indoor recess, as choices when other work is finished, and for homework. Consider making "game packs" for such times by placing the directions and needed materials in resealable plastic bags. Students can check them out during free times or take them home to play with a family member.

All About Math Workshop

Math Workshop provides an opportunity for students to work on a variety of activities that usually focus on similar mathematical content. The activities are not sequential; as students move among them, they continually revisit the important concepts and ideas they are learning. By repeatedly playing a game, or solving similar problems, students are able to refine strategies, use different contexts, and bring new knowledge to familiar experiences. Math Workshop is designed to:

- Provide students with repeated experience with the concepts being learned and time to practice important skills and refine strategies

- Provide time for the teacher to work with individuals and small groups and to assess students' learning and understanding

- Help students develop independence and learn to take responsibility for their own learning as they choose activities, keep track of their work, use and take care of classroom materials, and work with others

It is important to structure Math Workshop in ways that work for you and your students. The following questions can guide decision-making about how to set up Math Workshop in your classroom. You may need to experiment before finding the way that works best for you and your students.

How should the activities be organized? How will the materials be made available?

Some teachers set activities up at centers or stations around the room. At each center, students find the materials needed to complete the activity. Others store materials in a central location and have students bring materials to their desks or tables. In either case, materials should be readily accessible to students, and students should be expected to take responsibility for cleaning up and returning materials to their appropriate storage locations. Giving students a "five minutes until cleanup" warning before the end of an activity session allows them to finish what they are working on and prepare for the upcoming transition.

How do I decide how many students can work on an activity at once?

Most teachers limit the number of students who work on a Math Workshop activity at one time. Because students often want to do a new activity immediately after it is introduced, you will need to reassure them that everyone will have repeated chances to do each activity. In many cases, the quantity of materials available limits the number of students who can do an activity at any one time. Even if this is not the case, set guidelines about the number of students that work on each choice. This gives students the opportunity to work in smaller groups and to make decisions about what they want and need to do. It also provides a chance to visit activities repeatedly.

How will the class know what the activities are, and how many students can work on an activity at once?

Primary teachers have different ways of communicating such information to students. For example, some list the activities on the board, on the overhead, or on a piece of chart paper, and sketch a picture next to each to help students who cannot yet read the activity names. Others use a pocket chart or laminate a piece of tag-board to create a Math Workshop board that they can easily update as new activities are added from session to session and old activities are no longer offered. For example:

Math Workshop

Pattern-Block Fill-ins	Talisa, Diego, Lyle
Fill the Hexagons	Seth, Marta, Emilia, Neil
Pattern-Block Counts	Leah, Libby, William, Toshi

Some teachers label each activity with a number, or with drawings of stick figures, to show how many students can do the activity at once. Others explain that the number of chairs at a particular table or station show how many students it can accommodate.

How do I help students make choices about the activities they will do, and use their time productively?

Initially you may need to help students plan what they do when. Support students in making decisions about the activities they do, rather than organizing students into groups and circulating the groups every fifteen minutes, or making Math Workshops whole class activities. Making choices, planning their time, and taking responsibility for their own learning are important aspects of students' school experiences. If some students return to the same activity over and over again without trying others, suggest that they make a different first choice and then do the favorite activity as a second choice. Other students may need to be encouraged to use their time efficiently to complete all activities.

In any classroom there will be a range of how much work students can complete. Making Math Workshop activities available at other times during the day allows students to revisit favorite activities; gives students who need it more time to finish their work; and can provide targeted practice for all students. Many Math Workshop activities include extensions and/or additional problems for students to do when they have completed their required work. You can also encourage students to return to activities they have done before, solve another problem or two, or play a game again.

How do I keep track, and help students keep track, of the activities they have completed and the work they have done?

Some teachers design a Math Workshop board that keeps track of which activities students are choosing. Some use a class list to jot notes as students make choices at the beginning of each Math Workshop. Others ask students to record the name and/or a picture of the activity on a blank sheet of paper when they have finished. Still others post a sheet for each activity—with the name and the corresponding picture—at the front of the room or at each station. When students have completed an activity, they print their name on the corresponding sheet.

Whenever students do work on paper during Math Workshop, you should handle this as you do any other completed or yet-to-be finished math work (e.g., a math folder, binder, desk, cubby, etc.). Keeping a date stamp at the front of the room (or at each Math Workshop station), makes it easy for students to record the date, which can also help you keep track of their work.

How do I help students work independently, cooperatively, and productively?

As you introduce Math Workshop, and as students experience it over time, it is critical to establish clear guidelines and to clearly communicate your expectations. Be sure to describe and discuss students' responsibilities:

- Be productively engaged during Math Workshop.

- Work on every activity [at least once].

- If you don't understand or feel stuck, [ask a friend]. (Some teachers establish an "ask three, then me" rule, requiring students to check with three peers before coming to the teacher for help.)

Plan to spend a few minutes at the end of Math Workshop, particularly early in the year, discussing what went smoothly, what sorts of issues arose and how they were resolved, and what students enjoyed or found difficult. Having students share the work they have been doing often sparks interest in an activity. Some days, you might ask two or three volunteers to talk about their work. On other days, you might pose a question that someone asked you during Math Workshop, so that other students might respond to it. Encourage students to be involved in the process of finding solutions to problems that come up in the classroom. In doing so, they take some responsibility for their own behavior and become involved with establishing classroom policies.

What should I be doing during Math Workshop?

Initially, much of your time during Math Workshop will be spent circulating around the classroom, helping students get settled into activities, monitoring the process of moving from one choice to another, and generally managing the classroom. Once routines are familiar and well established, students will become more independent and responsible for their work during Math Workshop. This will allow you to spend more concentrated periods of time observing the class as a whole or working with individuals and small groups.

Once Math Workshop is running smoothly, this structure provides you with the opportunity to observe and listen to students while they work. Because students are working on different activities at the same time, you can structure and adapt activities to fit their varying needs. Also, you can meet with individual students, pairs, or small groups who need help or more challenge, or whom you haven't had a chance to observe before, or to do individual assessments. Recording your observations of students will help you keep track of how they are interacting with materials and solving problems. See *Assessment in This Unit,* which offers some strategies for recording and using observations of students.

PART 3

Mathematics in Grade 1

Number and Operations: Whole Numbers

Counting and the Number System

Throughout first grade, students work on developing strategies for accurately counting a group of up to 50 objects. They have repeated practice with the counting sequence, both forward and backward, and with counting and keeping track of sets of objects. They also connect the number names with the written numbers and the quantities that they represent.

5

Five

* * * * *

As students are developing accurate counting strategies, they are also building an understanding of how the numbers in the counting sequence are related—each number is one more (or one less) than the number before (or after) it. As students build this understanding, they compare and order quantities and develop a sense of the relative size of the numbers and the quantities they represent.

Students also make sense of counting by numbers other than 1. They connect the number sequence of counting by 2s, 5s, and 10s to the quantities they represent. As they work on activities that involve multiple groups of the same amount, they build an understanding that as they say each number in the counting sequence, they are adding 2, 5, or 10 more things. This leads to more efficient and accurate counting.

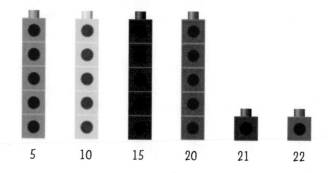

5   10   15   20   21   22

Mathematical Emphases

Counting and Quantity

- Developing strategies for accurately counting a set of objects by ones and by groups

- Developing an understanding of the magnitude and position of numbers

Benchmarks (Compiled from Units 1, 3, and 8)

- Count a set of up to 20 objects.

- Compare and order quantities up to 12.

- Count a set of 40–50 objects.

- Rote count, read, and write numbers to 65.

- Begin to count by groups in meaningful ways.

- Identify, read, write, and sequence numbers to 105.

Addition and Subtraction

In first grade, students work with the important idea that quantities can be composed and decomposed in different ways, while the quantity remains the same. Students have repeated experiences breaking one number (a whole) into two parts or combining two parts to form a whole. They consider the relationship between the parts, noticing, for example, that when the whole remains the same, as one part increases the other part decreases. Students work with composing and decomposing numbers up to 20 and focus on the addition combinations of 10. Students are expected to develop fluency with the combinations of 10 by the end of the school year.

There are 8 pieces of fruit in your basket. Some are apples and some are bananas. How many of each could there be?

$$7 + 1$$
$$6 + 2$$
$$5 + 3$$
$$4 + 4$$
$$3 + 5$$
$$2 + 2$$
$$1 + 7$$

A student uses an ordered list to organize his responses to a How Many of Each? *problem*

The addition and subtraction work of first grade focuses on making sense of these operations, practicing adding and subtracting single-digit numbers, and solving addition and subtraction story problems. Many of the games and activities involve students in comparing and combining two amounts or removing one amount from the other, which offers practice with single-digit addition and subtraction. The goal of the work with story problems is for students to learn to visualize the action of story problems and to solve the problems in ways that make sense to them.

By the end of the school year, it is expected that first graders will *count on* to combine two small quantities and that some students will use a combination they know to solve related problems (e.g., $6 + 4 = 10$, so $6 + 5 = 11$). For subtraction, many students will still show all, remove some, and count those that remain. Others will count back, count up, or use relationships they know (e.g., $14 - 5 = 14 - 4 - 1$).

1. There were 14 children playing in the park.
   Then 5 children went home.
   How many children were still in the park?

A sample subtraction problem from the Student Activity Book

I now the ~~o\s~~ answer
is 9 because you take
away 13, 12, 11, 10 9
the reson thier these nubers
here is because I want
lm to make sure
that I am ~~conting~~
takieng away 5.
14 - 5 = 9

Count back

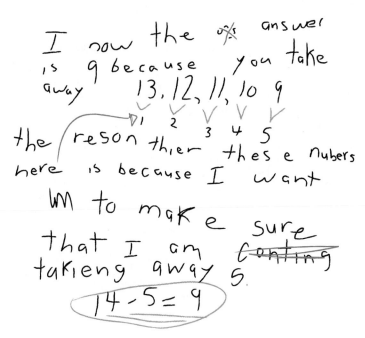
1 2 3 4 5 6 7 8 9 10 11 12 13 14
1 2 3 4 5 6 7 8 9

14 - 5 = 9

9

Show all, remove or cross out some, and then count how many are left

if I take away
the 4 from 14
it is 10 take away 1 it is 9
14 - 5 = 9

Use a combination you know

Students use mathematical tools, such as cubes and counters, and representations, such as the number line and 100 chart, to model and solve addition and subtraction problems and to clarify and communicate their thinking. They are encouraged to represent their work on paper in ways that make sense to them. Many use a combination of pictures, words, numbers, and mathematical symbols.

Mathematical Emphases

Number Composition

• Representing numbers by using equivalent expressions

• Composing numbers up to 20 with two addends

Whole Number Operations

• Making sense of and developing strategies to solve addition and subtraction problems with small numbers

• Using manipulatives, drawings, tools, and notation to show strategies and solutions

Computational Fluency

• Knowing addition combinations of 10

- Combine two small quantities.

- Find more than one combination of two addends for a number up to 10 (e.g., 7 is 4 and 3 and is also 5 and 2).

- Find at least five two-addend combinations of 10.

- Interpret (retell the action and sequence) and solve addition story problems.

- Subtract one small quantity from another.

- Represent numbers by using equivalent expressions.

- Find at least five combinations of two addends for a number up to 15.

- Combine two small quantities by at least counting on.

- Demonstrate fluency with the two-addend combinations of 10.

- Interpret (retell the action and sequence) and solve addition and subtraction story problems.

Geometry

The emphasis of geometry work in first grade is on careful observation, description, and comparison of two-dimensional (2-D) and three-dimensional (3-D) geometric shapes.

Students describe 2-D shapes, sort and compare them, and think about questions like the following: What makes a triangle a triangle? How are triangles different from squares?

Developing visual images of shapes as well as drawing 2-D shapes are two ways in which students come to know the important features of shapes. When they sort 2-D shapes, they make groups of shapes that "go together," which requires them to look for similarities and differences among the attributes of different shapes.

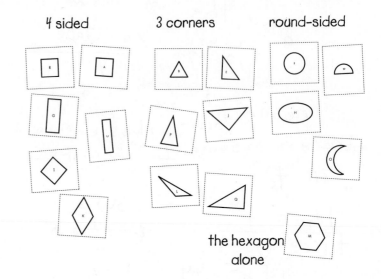

One pair's sorting of Shape Cards

Students look for 3-D shapes in their own environment, and they work with 3-D shapes (whose faces are familiar 2-D shapes) such as Geoblocks, manufactured boxes, and boxes made by students.

Students also learn about geometric relationships by composing and decomposing shapes. As they fill in the same shape outline with pattern blocks in different ways, they break apart or combine shapes to create a given shape. When using the Geoblocks, for example, students notice that two cubes can be put together to make a rectangular prism and that two triangular prisms can be put together to make a cube.

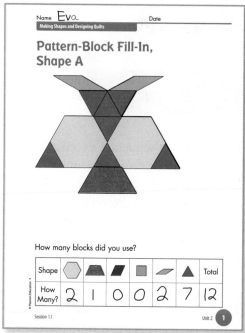

Eva counted up each kind of block accurately, then found the total this way: "7 + 2 is 8, 9, and 2 more is 10, 11, then 1 is 12."

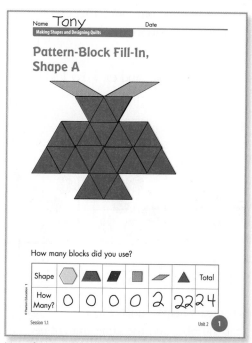

Tony also counted the blocks carefully, then found the total by adding 2 onto 22.

Students investigate the relationship between 3-D shapes and 2-D representations of those shapes. By matching 3-D objects to the outlines of their faces, to pictures, and to drawings by other students, they identify shapes by looking carefully at some parts of the shape and then visualizing what the whole shape looks like. Moving back and forth between 3-D objects and their 2-D representations helps students describe and compare the characteristics of common 3-D shapes.

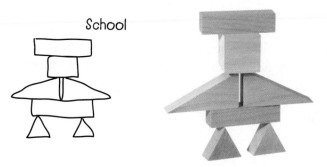

A student draws a 2-D representation of his 3-D building.

The *Shapes* Software is introduced as a tool for extending and deepening this work. This tool is designed for K–2 students to explore how different shapes can be combined to form other shapes, experiment with different types of geometric transformations (rotation, translation, reflection), make patterns, and investigate symmetry.

Mathematical Emphases

Features of Shapes

- Composing and decomposing 2-D shapes

- Describing, identifying, and comparing 2-D and 3-D shapes

- Exploring the relationships between 2-D and 3-D shapes

Benchmarks

- Fill a given region in different ways with a variety of shapes.

- Use geometric language to describe and identify important features of familiar 2-D shapes.

- Identify and describe triangles.

- Describe and sort 2-D shapes.

- Compose and decompose shapes.

- Attend to features of 3-D shapes, such as overall size and shape, the number and the shape of faces, and the number of corners.

- Match a 2-D representation to a 3-D shape or structure.

Patterns and Functions

Students begin their work with patterns in first grade by creating, describing, extending, and making predictions about repeating patterns. By building or acting out these patterns and thinking about how the pattern continues, students analyze the regularities of the pattern to determine what comes next or what will come several steps ahead in the pattern. Students analyze the structure of a repeating pattern by identifying the *unit* of the pattern—the part of the pattern that repeats over and over. By focusing on the unit of the repeating pattern, students shift their focus from seeing that "red follows yellow and yellow follows red" to how the repeating pattern is constructed as an iterated red-yellow unit. This focus allows students to analyze more complex patterns.

Students also compare patterns and begin to notice how patterns are the same. For example, a red, yellow, red, yellow pattern and a green, blue, green, blue pattern have the same structure.

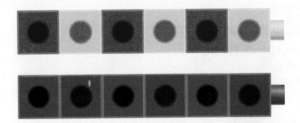

Students then work with number sequences associated with repeating patterns. Associating the counting numbers with a repeating pattern allows new kinds of questions about the pattern, such as the following: "What color will the 17th square be?" "Is the 20th square black?" Numbering the elements of a repeating pattern provides another way to describe the pattern.

Students also consider situations that have a constant increase. They investigate three different contexts—collecting pennies in a jar, making Staircase Towers from connecting cubes, and making repeating patterns with pattern blocks. In each situation, a sequence of numbers is generated by the situation.

Example: I have one penny in a jar, and each day I add three more pennies.

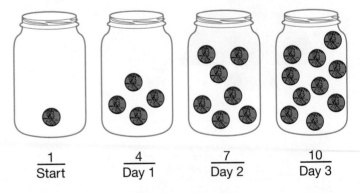

Comparison across contexts helps students focus on how the same start number and the same amount of constant increase can create the same number sequence in different situations.

Mathematical Emphases

Repeating Patterns

- Constructing, describing, and extending repeating patterns

- Identifying the unit of a repeating pattern

Number Sequences

- Constructing, describing, and extending number sequences with constant increments generated by various contexts

Benchmarks

- Construct, describe, and extend a repeating pattern with the structure AB, ABC, AAB, or ABB.

- Identify the unit of a repeating pattern for patterns with the structure AB or ABC.

- Describe how various AB or ABC patterns are alike (e.g., how is a red-blue pattern like a yellow-green pattern?).

- Determine what comes several steps beyond the visible part of an AB, ABC, AAB, or ABB repeating pattern.

- Construct, extend, and describe a pattern that has a constant increase for the sequences 1, 3, 5, . . . ; 2, 4, 6, . . . ; 1, 4, 7, . . . ; 2, 5, 8, . . . ; and 3, 6, 9, . . . through counting and building.

Data Analysis

In first grade, students sort groups of related objects, such as buttons, into groups and describe what distinguishes one group from another. This early work in classification provides experience in considering only certain attributes of an object while ignoring others. Sorting a variety of sets lays the foundation for later work in classifying shapes and numbers and in working with categorical data.

A student sorts a set of buttons into two groups: "fancy" and "not fancy."

First graders create their own representations of the data they collect, organizing their data and providing an image that helps them describe what the data show. Students are also introduced to several standard forms of representation, including picture graphs, tallies, charts, and bar graphs. By discussing and comparing representations, students consider what features of a representation help communicate a clear description of the data. As students describe data, the key question they consider is: "What do these data tell us about our class [or the class next door or our siblings]?" In the context of this overall question, first graders' descriptions focus on two characteristics of the data: (1) "What is the number of pieces of data in each category or at each value?" and (2) "Which category has more data?"

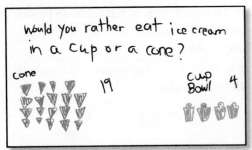

Survey question: Would you rather eat ice cream in a cup or in a cone?

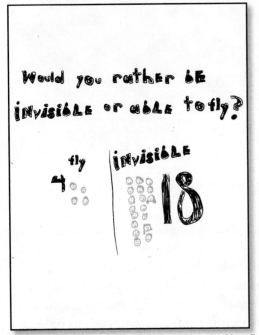

Survey question: Would you rather be invisible or be able to fly?

Students carry out their own data investigation. They develop a question, collect the data, represent the data, and describe and interpret the data, which may, in turn, bring up more questions. Once data are collected, the data are represented, examined, and analyzed to find out what information the data provide about the original questions.

Mathematical Emphases

Data Analysis

- Sorting and classifying

- Representing data

- Describing data

- Designing and carrying out a data investigation

Benchmarks

- Sort a group of objects according to a given attribute.

- Represent a set of data with two categories.

- Interpret a variety of representations of data with two categories.

- Describe a set of data, including how many are in each group, which group is greater, and how many people responded to the survey.

Measurement

It is important for students to develop a sense of how measurement is used—and when it is helpful—in the real world. Unit 5, *Fish Lengths and Animal Jumps,* involves students in a real context in which measuring is used, that of measuring fish to determine if they are "keepers." They measure relatively small lengths (up to 18 inches) and longer distances (up to 5–6 feet) and see that measurement is applied to both objects and distances.

The focus of the unit is on developing a foundation of skills for accurate linear measurement, such as knowing where to start and stop measuring, understanding how measuring tools must be lined up so that there are no gaps or overlaps, knowing which dimension to measure, measuring the shortest line from point to point, and understanding that many measurements are not reported in whole numbers. Regardless of what is measured, students learn that when one measures an object twice—or when two different people measure it—the same results should be obtained, assuming that the same measuring unit is used. Students also explore what happens when something is measured with small units versus larger units. Students begin to see that measuring an object in cubes will result in a different count than will measuring the same object in inch tiles or paper clips, but they may not yet see the inverse relationship between the size of the unit and the number of units needed to cover a distance.

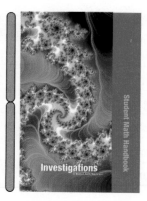

Mathematical Emphases

Linear Measurement

- Understanding length

- Using linear units

- Measuring with standard units

Benchmarks

- Demonstrate measuring techniques when measuring a distance with nonstandard or standard units. These techniques include starting at the beginning, ending at the end, leaving no gaps or overlaps, measuring in a straight line, and keeping track of the number of units.

- Know at least one way of describing a measurement that falls between two whole numbers.

- Understand that the same results should be obtained when the same object is measured twice or when two different people measure the same object (using the same unit).

- Understand that measuring with different-sized units will result in different numbers.

PART 4

Classroom Routines

Curriculum Unit	1	2	3	4	5	6	7	8	9
Classroom Routines									
Start With/Get To	•	•	•	•	•	•	•	•	
Morning Meeting	•	•	•	•	•	•	•	•	•
Quick Images	•	•	•	•	•	•		•	•
Tell a Story							•	•	•
Quick Survey				•	•	•	•		•

Preview

Classroom Routines and Ten-Minute Math activities offer practice and review of key concepts at each grade level. The two types of activities differ mainly in how and when they are integrated into your class day. Classroom Routines appear throughout Grades K–2, and two are included in Grade 3. Ten-Minute Math activities appear in Grades 3–5.

Classroom Routines occur at regular intervals, perhaps during morning meeting, at the beginning of math class, or at another convenient time. These short activities, designed to take no longer than 10 minutes, support and balance the in-depth work of each curriculum unit. After their first introduction in a math session, they are intended for use outside of math time. Some teachers use them to bring the whole class together just before or after lunch or recess or at the beginning or end of the day.

At Grade 1, five Classroom Routines are woven through the nine curriculum units. The following pages contain complete procedures for these activities, including the variations intended for use in Grade 1. Specific suggestions for use are found in Today's Plan for each session. It is recommended that you begin with the suggested daily problems and adapt them to fit the needs of your students throughout the year. Any needed preparation is noted in the Investigation Planner.

Start With/Get To

A "start with" and a "get to" number are chosen from a set of number cards. Students identify the numbers, find them on the class number line, and then count from one to the other.

Math Focus Points

Start With/Get To helps students develop fluency with the rote counting sequence, both forward and backward. It also helps them connect numerals (e.g., 15) to their number names (e.g., fifteen) and develop a sense of the magnitude and relationship among numbers.

◆ Connecting written numbers and number names

◆ Using the number line as a tool for counting

◆ Practicing the forward and backward counting sequences with numbers up to 100

Start With/Get To is introduced in Sessions 2.1 and 2.5 in Unit 1, *How Many of Each?*

Materials

- Resource Masters, *Start With/Get To* Cards

- A basket or bin to hold the *Start With/Get To* cards

- Class number line, posted at students' eye level

- Clothespins, ideally in green and red, for marking the "start with" and "get to" numbers

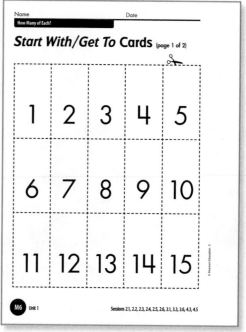

▲ Resource Masters, Unit 1 M6

Basic Activity

Step 1 **Explain whether you will "start with" 1 or "get to" 1.** "If you **Start with 1**, explain that your "start with" number will be 1 and mark it on the number line, perhaps with a green clothespin." Ask a volunteer to choose a "get to" number from the basket of *Start With/Get To* cards. Ask students what number is shown on the card and work together to find it on the class number line. Mark it, perhaps with a red clothespin.

If you **get to 1**, explain that your "get to" number will be 1 and mark it on the number line, perhaps with a red clothespin. Ask a volunteer to choose a "start with" number from the basket of *Start With/Get To* cards. Ask students what number is shown on the card and work together to find it on the class number line. Mark it, perhaps with a green clothespin.

Step 2 **As a class, count from the "start with" number to the "get to" number.** Keep track of the count on the class number line.

A class counts in the Classroom Routine Start With/Get To.

Variations

Different Ways to Count

Instead of counting as a whole class, sometimes students count around the class, partner up to count, or work individually to write the numbers. Other times students count on the 100 chart instead of the number line.

Two Baskets

Materials

• Resource Masters, *Start With/Get To* Cards, Sets 1, 2, and 3

• A basket labeled "Start With" and another labeled "Get To"

• Paper and pencil per student (depending on the daily write-up)

• Class 100 chart and transparent markers in green and red (depending on the daily write-up)

This variation focuses on two types of counting:

Counting Forward   Choose the "start with" number from a basket holding the numbers 1–15 and the "get to" number from a basket holding the numbers 16–30. As in the basic activity, students identify the numbers, mark them on the number line, and then count from one to the other. For example,

Jacob said that Keena picked the number [11] from our "start with" basket. Sacha, can you clip our "start with" pin to 11?

What number did Teo pick? [27] Stacy, can you clip our "get to" pin on [27]?

Okay, we are going to start with [11] and get to [27]. Let's count!

Later in the year, the "start with" basket holds the numbers up to 30, and then 50, while the "get to" basket holds the numbers 31–50, and then 51–100.

Counting Backward   Choose the "start with" number from a basket holding the numbers 16–30 and the "get to" number from a basket holding the numbers to 1–15. As in the basic activity, students identify the numbers, mark them on the number line, and then count from one to the other. For example,

What number did Toshi pick? [23] Sacha, can you clip our "start with" pin to [23]?

Richard says that Emilia's number is [15]. Emilia, can you clip our "get to" pin to [15]?

Okay, we are going to start with [23] and get to [15]. Vic says that means we are counting backward; let's count!

Later in the year, the "start with" basket holds the numbers 31–50, and then 51–100, while the "get to" basket holds the numbers up to 30, and then up to 50.

One Basket

Materials

- Resource Masters, *Start With/Get To* Cards, Sets 1, 2, and 3

- A basket

- Paper and pencil per student (depending on the daily write-up)

- Class 100 chart and transparency markers in green and red (depending on the daily write-up)

Place all of the *Start With/Get To* cards—the numbers up to 30, 50, or 100—in one basket. Students choose both the "start with" and "get to" numbers from this basket. As in the basic activity, they identify the numbers and mark them on the number line. In this variation, the discussion should focus on whether the class will be counting forward (up) or backward (down) and how you know. Then count together as a class, keeping track of the count on the class number line.

Counting by Groups

Math Focus Point

◆ Counting by 5s and 10s

Materials

- Resource Masters, *Start with/Get to* Cards, Sets 1, 2, and 3

- A basket labeled "Start With" and another labeled "Get To"

- Paper and pencil (depending on daily write-up)

- Class 100 chart and transparency markers in green and red (depending on daily write-up)

Set aside the 5, 10, and 100 cards. When you do the routine, pull the 10 card from the "start with" basket, and the 100 card from the "get to" basket. Explain that instead of counting by 1s, today you will practice counting by 10s. Count aloud as a class, while keeping track on a number line or a 100 chart. Repeat this activity using 5 as your "start with" card. Count by 5s to 100, keeping track on a number line or a 100 chart.

Morning Meeting

Students count to take attendance, use the calendar to establish the day and date, review the day's schedule, and record the day's weather. Spending 5–10 minutes each day on this set of four activities helps establish routines and structures that students will revisit, use, and build on throughout the year as they develop fluency with counting; learn to describe and interpret data; and explore the structure of time in the context of a school day, a month, a week, or a year.

Math Focus Points

Morning Meeting takes activities common to many first-grade classrooms and focuses on the mathematics inherent in them.

◆ Developing strategies for counting accurately (Attendance, Calendar, Weather)

◆ Using the calendar as a tool for keeping track of time (Calendar)

◆ Developing vocabulary to talk about time, such as "morning," "noon," "midday," and "afternoon," and sequence, such as "first," "next," "last," "before," and "after." (Daily Schedule, Calendar)

◆ Collecting and recording data (Weather)

Morning Meeting is introduced over the course of Sessions 1.1–1.3 in Unit 1, *How Many of Each?*

Preparation

● Prepare and post a pocket (or write-on/wipe-off) calendar for the current month. Show all of the dates and mark any special occasions (e.g., a visitor or field trip). (Some teachers pencil in the numbers so that students can trace them as part of the daily routine.)

A sample classroom calendar for September

● Cut apart and post a yearlong calendar to make a wall display of a whole year (September to August or January to December).

- Prepare and post a Daily Schedule that identifies the schedule of the day's events (e.g., the start of school, morning meeting, reading, lunch, recess, music, math, and science) with symbols and/or pictures as well as words.

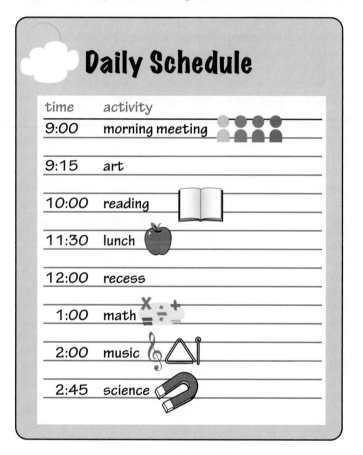

- Prepare and post a weather chart for recording the data about the current month's weather, using categories appropriate for your climate and for first graders.

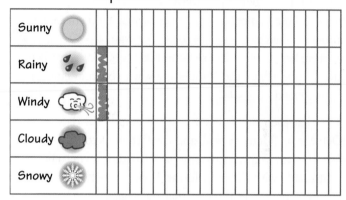

A sample weather chart for the current month

- Prepare and post a yearlong weather data chart, using one-inch grid paper to make a 10-by-10 grid for each weather category your class chooses.

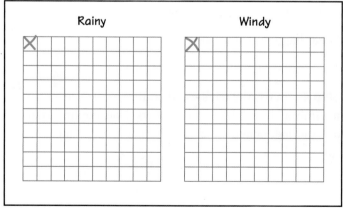

A sample yearlong weather data chart

Basic Activity

Step 1 Take attendance. Count the number of students present in at least two different ways.

Step 2 Using the Calendar, work together to determine the day and date. Count up to today's date and help students connect those numbers to quantities by relating them to the number of days in the month so far. For example, "1, 2, 3, 4, 5. So, there have been 5 days so far in [October]." (Some teachers have a student trace the number as a way to build in number writing practice.)

Note that there are different ways to refer to the date: [October 5], [October 5th], and the [5th of October]. Vary the way you refer to dates so that students become comfortable with different forms. Saying "the [5th day of October]" reinforces the idea that the calendar is a way to keep track of days in a month.

Step 3 Discuss the day's schedule with students. Ask students to use the schedule to respond to questions like the following:

What will we do first today? What happens next?

What will we do after math?

What happens before lunch?

What's the last thing will we do today?

Step 4 Discuss the day's weather. Record the data on your monthly and yearlong weather charts. Note the importance of recording more than one description if, for example, it is sunny and windy.

What's the Math?

Attendance   Counting the class each day helps students develop strategies for counting accurately. Because it is important data (e.g., it must be submitted to the office daily), attendance offers a particularly good context for conversations about strategies for counting and keeping track, the importance of accuracy, and the need for double-checking a count.

Calendar   This routine helps students see and use the calendar as a real-world tool for keeping track of time and events. It provides a regular review of the names and sequences of the days and months; an opportunity to explore the relationships among days, weeks, and months; and regular practice with the numbers and counting sequence to 31.

Daily Schedule   Discussing the daily schedule provides students with opportunities to hear, understand, and use time-related words, such as *first, next, last, before, after, during, early, later,* and *at the beginning (or end) of.*

Weather   Keeping track of weather engages students in collecting real-life data that changes over time.

Variations

Attendance: How Many Now?

Math Focus Points

◆ Estimating quantities up to about 30

◆ Adding small amounts to or subtracting small amounts from a familiar number

In this variation, students estimate and then determine the number of students present when several students are missing or when the class has visitors. Ask questions like the following:

Everyone is here today. Teo and Carol just went to the office with our attendance. How many students are in our room now? How do you know?

When we took attendance, there were 25 students. But Sacha just arrived. How many do we have now? How do you know?

Encourage students to estimate first, particularly when problems involve several missing (or extra) students:

The children at Diego's and Leah's tables just went to the nurse. Usually we have 28 students. Look around. About how many students do you think are here right now? Do you think there are more than 5? more than 10? more than 20?

Then try several of the students' suggestions for finding the exact number. Typical strategies include counting all of the students, adding the number of students at each table, or counting on or back from the number of students in the class.

Over the course of the year, this context enables students to explore different ways to compose and decompose a number (the number of students in your class). Ask questions like the following:

If everyone is here, we have 28 students in our class. Nicky and Neil are both absent today. How many students are here today? How do you know?

Yesterday we had 26 students in our class. Look around. How many students do you think are here today? Why do you think so?

Many students count from one. However, because they are important and familiar quantities, some students begin to reason about the quantities involved to solve such problems.

"Yesterday we had 26 students, and Marta and Chris were both absent. Today Chris came back, so we have one more person, so there must be 27 today."

"Well, we have 28 students in our class when everyone is here. Now only Marta is absent, so it is one less. So it is 27."

Attendance: Can Everyone Have a Partner?

Math Focus Point

◆ Investigating numbers that can (and cannot) be made into groups of two

Taking attendance offers an opportunity for forming and counting by groups of two. This variation involves questions like the following:

[Twenty-six] students are here today. Do you think that everyone can have a partner? How do you know?

Students share ideas and strategies, which typically include putting [26] cubes or stick figures or kids into groups of two, using the seating arrangement to visualize whether everyone could have a partner, and counting by 2s to see if you say the total number of students. Later in the year, some students begin to reason: "I know 13 doesn't work, because you can do it with 12; 13 is one more, so you can't do it." Discuss students' ideas and try them out.

A Note About Counting by 2s

Use this variation as an opportunity to expose students to counting by 2s in a familiar and engaging context. Though many first graders know the counting by 2s sequence, they may not connect this "song" to the quantities the numbers represent. Therefore, when the class counts together by 2s, have students say the first number in the pair softly and the second one loudly: "one, TWO, three, FOUR, ..." Hearing all of the numbers helps students keep track of how the counting matches the number of people.

Calendar: A New Month

At the start of each month, change the monthly calendar to show the new month. Ask students what they notice about the new month. Some students focus on the arrangement of numbers or the total number of days, while others note special events or pictures or designs on the calendar. To help students see that a month is part of a larger whole, ask students to find the position of the new month on the yearlong calendar display.

As the year progresses, encourage students to make comparisons between the months. Post the calendar for the new month next to the calendar for the month just ending and ask students to share their ideas about how the two calendars are similar and different.

Calendar: Review

This variation provides an opportunity to review the following:

- **The Days of the Week.** Use the calendar to review the days of the week, noting which days are school days and which are weekend (or nonschool) days. Use an equation to represent this information. For example, $5 + 2 = 7$ for a typical week and $4 + 3 = 7$ for a week with a vacation day.

- **The Months of the Year.** Use the yearlong calendar display to review the names and sequence of the months of the year.

Calendar: How Many Days . . . ?

Ask students to figure out how long until (or since) a special event, such as a birthday, vacation, class trip, or holiday. Ask questions like the following:

Today is [October 5]. How many more days until [October 15]?

How many more days until [the storyteller comes to visit]?

How many days has it been since our [field trip to the aquarium]?

Students use the calendar to determine how many days and share their strategies for figuring this out. Initially, many students count each day. Later, some students begin to use their growing knowledge of the calendar's structure and number relationships. Here are some examples:

"I knew there were 3 more days in this row, and I added them to the 3 days in the next row. That's 6 more days."

"Today is the 5th. Five more days is 10, and 5 more is 15. That's 10 more days until October 15."

For more challenge, ask questions that span two calendar months. For example, post two months side by side and ask:

It is [April 29] today. How many more days until [our class trip on May 6]?

You can also use the yearlong calendar display to ask students such questions. For example,

Last week was our February vacation. How many weeks until the next vacation?

Calendar: Mixed Up Calendar

Choose two or three dates (or cards for the days of the week) and change their position on the calendar so that they are out of order. Ask students to find the mistakes and help you fix them.

Pairs or groups can play this game during free time. Students can also remove all the date cards except the first one, mix them up, and reassemble the calendar in the correct order.

The Daily Schedule: Time of Day

Encourage students to think about the times of day when daily activities happen, rather than just the sequence of what comes first, next, and last.

What are we doing this morning?

What do we have in the middle of the day today, at noon time?

What is happening this afternoon?

The Daily Schedule: Time

Math Focus Points

◆ Naming and telling time to the hour on digital and analog clocks

◆ Associating times on the hour with daily events

Materials

• Large demonstration clock

Include the time of events on the schedule, using both analog (clock face) and digital (e.g., 10:00) representations. Encourage students to think about what time different activities happen, focusing as much as possible on activities that start on the hour. Ask questions like the following:

What's happening at 9:00 this morning? [science]

What time does math start? [10:00]

This can evolve into discussions about telling time to the hour. Use the large demonstration clock to model such ideas as the following:

Science started at [9:00] and ended at [10:00]. We did science for 1 hour. Watch as I show that on the clock. What do you notice?

If we spend an hour doing math, what time do you think it will it be when we finish? Let's try it on the clock and see.

The discussion should focus on the position and movement of the hands.

A Note About Telling Time The focus of this variation is on becoming familiar with the notation of times on the hour and beginning to tell time to the hour. Students learn how to tell time to the hour, half hour, and quarter hour in the Grade 2 *Investigations* units; they learn to tell time to the minute in the Grade 3 *Investigations* units.

Weather: Discussing the Monthly Data

Math Focus Points

◆ Counting, describing, and comparing data

◆ Making sense of a variety of representations of data

Toward the end of each month, discuss the weather data you have collected. Ask questions like the following:

What is this graph about? What does this graph tell us about the weather we had this month?

What type of weather did we have for the most days? What type of weather did we have for the fewest number of days?

How many days were [sunny]? How many were [rainy]? Were there more [rainy] days or more [sunny] days?

How is the weather this month different from the weather last month? What were you looking at on the graph to help you figure that out?

How do you think the weather graph for next month will look? Why do you think so?

Weather: A New Month

Math Focus Point

◆ Making sense of a variety of representations of data

Each month, post a new monthly weather chart, varying the way you collect the data. Introduce it to students and encourage them to comment on how the representation is the same or different from the previous month's. Different representations suggested in the Grade 1 *Investigations* units include the following formats:

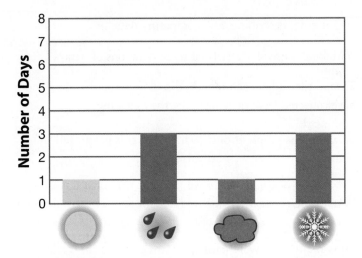

The weather in February

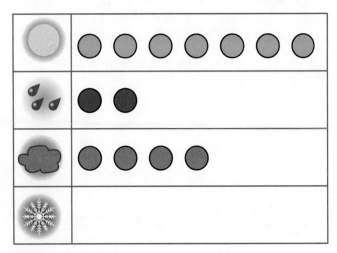

The weather in March

Sunny	☀ ☀ ☀
Cloudy	☁
Rainy	🌧 🌧

The weather in May

Weather: Discussing the Yearly Data

Math Focus Point

◆ Counting, describing, and comparing data

Ask students to consider the yearlong data collected so far. Choose one category and ask:

Take a minute and look at the data about [rainy] days. How many days has it been [rainy] so far this year? How do you know?

Have students share their strategies for calculating the total number of rainy days. While most count by 1s, some may use the rows of 10, particularly as the year progresses. For example,

"That's 10, and another 10 is 20, and 21, 22, 23. Twenty-three days have been [rainy]."

Quick Images

In this activity, students analyze dot images. After seeing an image for only a few seconds, students either draw or build a copy of it, based on the mental image they form during the brief viewing. The discussion should focus on what they saw, how they remembered the image, and how that helped them accurately re-create it.

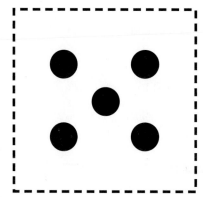

Dot Cards, Set A, Number 5

Math Focus Points

Students analyze, describe, re-create, and form their own visual images of quantities up to 10.

◆ Developing and analyzing visual images for quantities up to 10

◆ Re-creating an arrangement of objects

◆ Finding the total of two or more single-digit quantities

Quick Images is introduced in Session 2.6 in Unit 1, *How Many of Each?*

Materials

- Overhead projector (If you don't have access to an overhead projector, use a copy machine to enlarge the images. Or draw them on chart paper.)

- Transparencies T2 and T7, *Dot Cards,* Sets A and B

- Transparency T24, *Dot Addition Cards*

- Counters such as pennies, chips, or buttons (about 10 per student)

- Paper and pencil (1 per student)

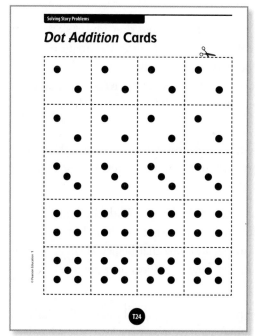

▲ **Resource Masters, Unit 3 M9; Transparencies, T24**

Basic Activity

Step 1 Flash an image for 3–5 seconds. Tell students that you will show an image of one or more Dot Cards for a short time. Encourage them to carefully study the image for the entire time it is visible. Explain that, when you turn off the projector (or hide the picture), students are to draw or build a copy of the image they see.

You may need to adjust the amount of time you flash the image. If you show it too long, you will see students simply copying the image from the screen, rather than building from their mental image; if you show it too briefly, students will not have time to form a mental image and will not be sure what to draw or build.

Step 2 Students draw or build what they saw. Ask students to choose whether they would like to draw the image or re-create it with counters; then give them time to do so. If students are concerned that they cannot recall the image exactly, assure them that they will have another chance to see it.

Step 3 Flash the image for another 3–5 seconds. This gives students an opportunity to refine and/or revise their mental image and their work.

Step 4 Show and discuss the image. With the image visible, ask students to describe what they saw, how they remembered the image, and how that helped them accurately re-create it. Also discuss how many dots there are in all and how they know.

Step 5 Follow Steps 1–4 with a related image. The daily routine write-up often suggests a set of two or three related numbers or combinations. For example, do *Quick Images* with the 4 from Set A and then with the 4 from Set B. Or do *Quick Images* with two 2s. Then show a 2 and a 3 and finally show two 3s.

Variations

Quick Images: Drawing Shapes

This variation is introduced in Session 1.3 in Unit 2, *Making Shapes and Designing Quilts.*

Math Focus Points

◆ Developing visual images of, and language for describing, 2-D shapes

◆ Identifying the names and attributes of 2-D shapes

Materials

- Transparencies, T14–T16, *Shape Cards*

- Transparencies T18, *Combination Shape Cards*

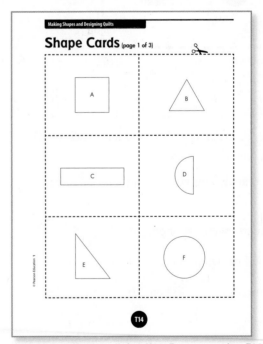

▲ **Resource Masters, Unit 2 M21; Transparencies, T14**

Display the suggested image. After the image is flashed, students draw what they saw. Class discussion focuses on the names and attributes of the shapes shown. Ask questions like the following:

What did you notice about the shape? Libby says it is a [square]. Who can say more about that?

What did you think about to help you draw the shape?

How would you describe this shape?

In addition, particularly for more challenging shapes, you can ask questions like the following:

What did you notice the first time you saw the shape?

Could you remember the whole shape?

What happened when you saw the shape the second time?

Did that help you add anything or change anything?

This variation also suggests occasionally asking students to compare different images at the end of a *Quick Images* session.

Quick Images: Squares

Math Focus Point

◆ Finding the total of two or more equals groups

◆ Exploring relationships among combinations

Materials

• Transparencies T28–T30, *Quick Images: Squares*

• Tiles or connecting cubes

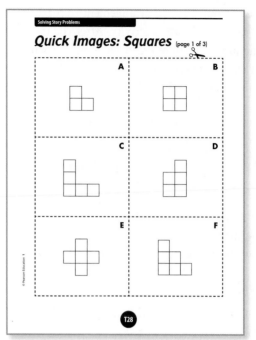

▲ Resource Masters, Unit 3 M32; Transparencies, T28

Display the suggested image and do the basic *Quick Images* activity. After the image is flashed, students use tiles or cubes to re-create the image. Focus the discussion on how students saw and remembered the groups of squares and how they found the total.

Quick Images: Coins

Math Focus Point

◆ Identifying and naming coins

Materials

• Overhead coins (class set)

Display the suggested number and arrangement of overhead coins and do the basic *Quick Images* activity. After the image is flashed, students use coins to re-create the image. Focus the discussion on the *type* of coins they saw, rather than on their *value*. Ask questions like the following:

Allie said there were four brown ones. What's the name of these brown coins [point to a penny]?

When I flashed the image, did anyone see a dime? Edgar, can you come up and show us which coin is a dime?

Also discuss how many coins—of each type and in all—students saw, how they remember the way they were arranged, and how that helped them re-create the image.

Quick Images: Ten-Frames

Quick Images: Ten-Frames is introduced in Session 1.4 in Unit 6, *Number Games and Crayon Puzzles.*

Math Focus Points

◆ Developing fluency with the addition combinations that make 10

◆ Using known combinations (e.g., combinations that make 10) to combine numbers

◆ Using standard notation (+, −, =) to write equations

Materials

• Transparency T45, *Ten-Frames*

• Resource Masters *Blank Ten-Frame* (1–2 per student)

• Pennies or other counters (10–20 per student)

Show the suggested image(s) and do the basic *Quick Images* activity. After the image is flashed, students use pennies or counters to re-create the image on a blank Ten-Frame. After doing single images (e.g., 7), this variation suggests showing 2 or more Ten-Frames. By specifying the numbers shown, for

example, 7 and 3, 4 and 6, or 5 and 5, this variation focuses on combinations that make 10. As you discuss the ways students saw the images, write equations that match their thinking, while circling the various groups of dots.

Felipe: "There's a row of 5 and then 3 more. That's 8."

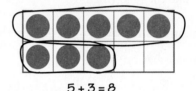

5 + 3 = 8

Jacinta: "I saw 3 groups of 2, so that's 2, 4, 6. And then 2 more is 8."

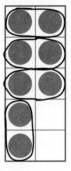

2 + 2 + 2 + 2 = 8

Diego: "If every square had 1, it would be 10, but 2 were empty. 10 − 2 = 8."

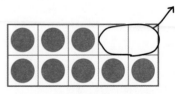

10 − 2 = 8

Tell a Story

Students generate a variety of story problems for a given addition or subtraction expression. Then they solve the problem and discuss their strategies.

Math Focus Points

Tell a Story helps students develop a meaningful understanding of standard notation (+, −, and =), and the actions and relationships such notation represents. It also provides them with regular addition and subtraction practice and with an opportunity to think about related problems.

◆ Connecting standard notation (+, −, =) to the actions and relationships they represent

◆ Creating a story problem for a given expression

◆ Developing strategies for adding and subtracting small numbers

◆ Solving related problems

Tell a Story is not introduced in a session; instead, it is suggested as a Classroom Routine beginning in Unit 7, *Color, Shape, and Number Patterns.*

Materials

• Chart paper

Basic Activity

Step 1 Write an addition or a subtraction expression on chart paper or the board. Because students should be familiar with both vertical and horizontal forms of notation, this routine varies the format used to present expressions to students. For example, write one of the following:

$$5 + 4 = \underline{\hphantom{xx}}$$
$$10 - 8 = \underline{\hphantom{xx}}$$

$$\begin{array}{r} 3 \\ + 6 \\ \hline \end{array} \qquad \begin{array}{r} 7 \\ - 2 \\ \hline \end{array}$$

Step 2 **Students generate story problems for a given expression.** Encourage students to think of a variety of kinds of stories.

Take a minute to look at what I have written on the board. Think about a story that could go with 5 + 4. What could happen? What could the 5 be? the 4?

Ask several students to share their stories and discuss them with the class. Here's an example:

What happens in Danielle's story? What was the 5? the 4? What about Seth's story?

Step 3 **Students solve the problem.** The discussion should focus on students' solution strategies. Ask questions like the following:

How did you solve the problem? Nicky held up 5 fingers on one hand, 4 fingers on the other hand, and then she counted all of her fingers.

Who solved the problem like Nicky?

Who did it a different way?

Step 4 **Repeat steps 1–3 with a related problem.** Present the second, related problem suggested in the daily routine write-up. For example, after telling stories and solving $5 + 4 = \underline{\hphantom{xx}}$, students tell a story for and solve $9 - 5 = \underline{\hphantom{xx}}$. Or, after telling stories and solving $10 - 8 = \underline{\hphantom{xx}}$, they then tell a story for and solve $8 + 2 = \underline{\hphantom{xx}}$. This provides an opportunity to discuss the relationship between addition and subtraction (e.g., if $5 + 4 = 9$, then $9 - 5 = 4$; and if $10 - 8 = 2$, then $8 + 2 = 10$).

Quick Survey

The teacher poses a survey question and uses a particular type of representation to represent students' responses. Students read the representation and interpret and describe the resulting data.

Math Focus Points

Quick Survey provides students with regular opportunities to collect, record, and discuss data. It is also designed to expose students to a variety of different ways to organize and record data.

◆ Collecting, counting, representing, describing, and comparing data

◆ Interpreting different representations of data, including pictures, bar graphs, tallies, and Venn diagrams

Quick Survey is introduced in Session 1.1 in Unit 4, *What Would You Rather Be?*

Materials

• Chart paper for making *Quick Survey* charts according to specifications

• Markers

• Stick-on notes or cubes (depending on the type of representation)

Basic Activity

Step 1 Prepare the *Quick Survey* **chart or other method for collecting the data, as suggested in the daily routine write-up.** Most of the time, this activity suggests using a survey question that results in only two responses. Occasionally, survey questions with multiple responses are suggested.

Step 2 Explain the survey. Explain the question students are to answer and the method you will be using to collect the data (e.g., writing their names, stick-on notes, tallies, etc.).

Step 3 Collect the data. The teacher collects or records students' responses as suggested in the daily routine write-up. Engage students in thinking about the data as you collect it. For example, if you are collecting data about whether students are right- or left-handed, ask questions like the following:

Are more people [right-handed] or [left-handed] so far?

Have I asked everybody? How do you know?

How many people have answered so far?

How many people have *not* answered?

One class used self-stick notes to collect and represent data.

Step 4 *Discuss the data.* Ask questions that encourage students to read the representation and to describe and interpret the data. Using the same example as in step 3, ask questions like the following:

How many people are [right handed]? How many people are [left-handed]?

Are there more [right-handed] or [left-handed] people in our class?

What else can you tell from this representation?

How many people responded to the survey? How do you know?

What's an equation that shows something we found out? [There are 24 right-handed people + 4 left-handed people, so 24 + 4 = 28.]

What do the data tell us about our class?

How do you think this survey might be helpful to me? [So you know how many righty and lefty scissors our class needs.]

Do you think we would get similar data if we collected on a different day? Why do you think so?

What if we did the same survey in another class? Would the results be the same or different? Why do you think so?

Do our results raise any new questions for you on this topic? [Would the numbers be the same if we ask which way people swing the bat? What if we asked about which foot you kick with?]

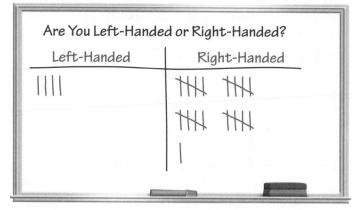

One class used tally marks to collect and represent data.

PART 5

Technology in *Investigations*

Preview

The *Investigations* curriculum incorporates two forms of technology: calculators and computers. In the early grades, students can begin to see how calculators can be used as mathematical tools. Computers are explicitly linked to one curriculum unit at each grade level through software that is provided with the curriculum.

Using Calculators with the Curriculum

During elementary school, students should become comfortable using a basic calculator as a tool that is common in their homes and communities. Increasingly sophisticated calculators are being developed and used in settings ranging from high school mathematics courses to science, business, and construction. Students need to learn how to use the calculator effectively and appropriately as a tool, just as they need to learn to read a clock, interpret a map, measure with a ruler, or use coins. They should use calculators for sensible purposes—just as you would do—not as a replacement for mental calculations or for pencil and paper calculations they are learning to do. While calculators are not explicitly used in first grade, you can encourage students to use calculators to double-check calculations, as an aid if they have many calculations to carry out outside of math class, or to solve problems for which they can think out a solution but don't yet have the experience to carry out the computation.

For example, in one primary classroom, students became interested in the number of days in the year. Although these students were not yet able to add a string of 12 double-digit numbers, they could articulate a sound strategy—adding the number of days in each month—and use a calculator to carry it out.

Look for situations in the classroom such as this one, where the purpose of the mathematical activity is not developing computational fluency and when the numbers and calculations are beyond the students' skills in written or mental computation. These situations provide opportunities for students to practice estimating reasonable results, then carrying out the calculation with a calculator.

Students enjoy using what they perceive as an adult tool. Investigating with the calculator gives students an opportunity to notice mathematical patterns and to ask questions about mathematical symbols. For example, in a second-grade class, students were dividing many numbers by 2, which led to a discussion of the meaning of 0.5. In a fourth-grade class, some students became intrigued with the square root sign. The teacher challenged them to systematically keep track of the results of applying the square root symbol to whole numbers, starting with 1, and to come up with an idea about its meaning.

The calculator is an efficient tool for many purposes in life, and students should learn to use it sensibly, knowing that using it well depends on the user's correct analysis and organization of the problem, comparing its results with reasonable estimates, and double-checking.

Introducing and Managing the *Shapes* Software in Grade 1

Shapes Software is provided as a component of the *Investigations* curriculum. The *Software Support Reference Guide* provides a complete description of the software and instructions for using the software activities.

The *Shapes* Software is formally introduced in Grade 1, Unit 2, *Making Shapes and Designing Quilts.* The software activities are integrated into Math Workshop and both extend and deepen the mathematical ideas emphasized in this curriculum unit. In some cases the software activities allow students to work with geometric shapes in ways that they are not able to in the noncomputer activities. Therefore, while using this software is optional, we recommend its use if you have computers either in your classroom or in your school's computer lab. Read the **Teacher Notes:** Introducing and Managing the *Shapes* Software (Unit 2, p. 125) and About the Math in the *Shapes* Software (Unit 2, p. 128) for further information about the software, about introducing and integrating computer work into your classroom, about the mathematics content of the activities, and about managing the computer environment.

Options for Introducing the *Shapes* Software

How you introduce and incorporate these computer activities into your curriculum depends on the number of computers and computer technology that you have available.

- *Computer lab:* If you have a computer laboratory with one computer for each pair of students, the entire class can become familiar with the computer activities at the same time. In this case, you will not need to devote time during math class to introduce the new software activity. Once an activity has been introduced, students can do it either during Math Workshop (if you have classroom computers) or during their scheduled lab time.

- *Large projection screen:* If you have a large projection screen, you can introduce the software activities to the whole class during a math session, immediately before Math Workshop or at another time of the day.

- *Small groups of students:* With fewer classroom computers, you can introduce the activities to small groups either before or during Math Workshop. These students can then be paired and become peer "teachers" of the software.

Regardless of the number of computers available, students generally benefit from working on these activities in pairs. This not only maximizes computer resources but also encourages students to consult, monitor, and teach one another. Generally, more than two students at one computer find it difficult to share. You may need to monitor computer use more closely than the other Math Workshop choices to ensure that all students get sufficient computer time. Each pair should spend at least 15–20 minutes at the computer for each activity.

Managing the Computer Environment

Students should be using the *Shapes* Software consistently throughout Unit 2 and periodically for the rest of the school year. If you have daily access to a computer lab, you might take advantage of this to supplement your regular math class. If your school has a computer teacher, you might collaborate with that teacher to have students work on *Shapes* activities during some of their scheduled lab time.

More typically, a classroom will have a small number of computers. With computers in the classroom, pairs of students can cycle through the software activities during Math Workshop, just as they cycle through the other choices. Three to five classroom computers is ideal, but even with only one or two, students can have a successful computer experience. When you have fewer computers, find additional computer time for students throughout the day, outside of math.

Using *Shapes* All Year

Unit 2 is the only unit in the Grade 1 sequence that explicitly uses the *Shapes* Software. However, we recommend that students continue using it for the remainder of the school year. With more experience, they become more fluent in the mechanics of the software itself and can better focus on the designs they want to make and how to select and arrange shapes for those designs. They can work with the tangram shapes as well as the pattern blocks and Power Polygon shapes, can solve the many different kinds of puzzles that come with the software, and make their own puzzles.

PART 6

Professional Development

Teacher Notes in *Investigations*

Teacher Notes are one of the most important professional development tools in *Investigations*. Each curriculum unit contains a collection of Teacher Notes that offer information about the mathematical content of that unit and how students learn it.

In this section of *Implementing Investigations in Grade 1,* you will find a set of Teacher Notes that addresses topics and issues applicable to the curriculum as a whole rather than to specific curriculum units.

These Teacher Notes provide important background about approaches to mathematics teaching and learning, about critical features of the mathematics classroom, and about how to develop an inclusive mathematics community in which all students participate. You can benefit from reading these notes, either individually or as the basis for discussion in teacher study groups, before starting to use the curriculum. Alternatively, you can read these notes gradually throughout the year while you are using the curriculum in your classroom. These brief essays take on new resonance and meaning as you have more experience with student learning and the *Investigations* curriculum. Plan to return to this collection periodically to review the ideas and reflect on the implications for classroom practice.

A complete list of the Teacher Note titles from each of the nine curriculum units is included on pages 71–72.

Computational Fluency and Place Value

Computational fluency includes accuracy, flexibility, and efficiency. When fluency with a particular operation is achieved, students can look at the problem as a whole, choose a solution strategy that they can carry out easily without becoming bogged down or losing track of their steps, use their strategy to solve the problem accurately, recognize whether the result is reasonable, and double-check their work. Students who are fluent have a repertoire that includes mental strategies, strategies in which only intermediate steps are jotted down while other steps are carried out mentally, and strategies that require a complete written solution. They are flexible in their choice of algorithm or procedure, and they can use one method to check another.

Developing computational fluency with whole numbers is central to the elementary curriculum. This development includes the building blocks of computation:

- Understanding the base-ten number system and its place value notation

- Understanding the meaning of the operations and their relationships

- Knowing the basic addition and multiplication number combinations (the "facts") and their counterparts for subtraction and division

- Estimating reasonable results

- Interpreting problems embedded in contexts and applying the operations correctly to these problems

- Learning, practicing, and consolidating accurate and efficient strategies for computing

- Developing curiosity about numbers and operations, their characteristics, and how they work

- Learning to articulate, represent, and justify generalizations

At each grade level, computational fluency looks different. Students are progressing in learning the meaning of the four arithmetic operations with whole numbers, developing methods grounded in this meaning, and gradually solving problems of greater difficulty through the grades. At each grade level, benchmarks for whole number computation indicate what is expected of all students by the end of each curriculum unit and each grade, although work at each grade level goes beyond these benchmarks. Gradually, approaches to problems become more efficient, flexible, and accurate. For example, in Grade 1, many students begin the year adding by direct modeling of the problem with objects and counting the sum by ones. By the end of the year, students are expected to start with one of the quantities and count on the other, and for some combinations students "just know" the sum or use known combinations to solve others ("I know $4 + 4 = 8$, so $4 + 5 = 9$"). In Grade 4, many students start the year solving some multiplication problems by skip counting, but by the end of the year, they are expected to solve multidigit multiplication problems such as 34×68 by breaking problems into subproblems, based on the distributive property.

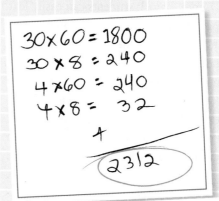

Sample Student Work

Understanding the Base-Ten Number System

Learning about whole number computation is closely connected to learning about the base-ten number system. The base-ten number system is a "place value" system. That is, any numeral, say 2, can represent different values, depending on where it appears in a written number: it can represent 2 ones, 2 tens, 2 hundreds, 2 thousands, as well as 2 tenths, 2 hundredths, and so forth. Understanding this place value system requires coordinating the way we write the numerals that represent a particular number (e.g., 217) and the way we name numbers in words (e.g., two hundred seventeen) with how those symbols represent quantities.

The heart of this work is relating written numerals to the quantity and to how the quantity is composed. It builds from work on tens and ones in Grades 1 and 2 to a focus on numbers in the hundreds and thousands in Grade 3, and work with numbers in the ten thousands, hundred thousands, and beyond in Grades 4 and 5. Knowing place value is not simply a matter of saying that 217 "has 2 hundreds, 1 ten, and 7 ones," which students can easily learn to do by following a pattern without attaching much meaning to what they are saying. Students must learn to visualize how 217 is built up from hundreds, tens, and ones, in a way that helps them relate its value to other quantities. Understanding the place value of a number such as 217 entails knowing, for example, that 217 is closer to 200 than to 300, that it is 100 more than 117, that it is 17 more than 200, that it is 3 less than 220, and that it is composed of 21 tens and 7 ones.

A thorough understanding of the base-ten number system is one of the critical building blocks for developing computational fluency. Understanding place value is at the heart of estimating and computing. For example, consider adding two different quantities to 32:

$32 + 30 = $ _____

$32 + 3 = $ _____

How much will 32 increase in each case? Students think about how the first sum will now have 6 tens, but the ones will not change, whereas in the second sum, the ones will change, but the tens remain the same. Adding three *tens* almost doubles 32, while adding three *ones* increases its value by a small amount. Considering the place value of numbers that are being added, subtracted, multiplied, or divided provides the basis for developing a reasonable estimate of the result.

The composition of numbers from multiples of 1, 10, 100, 1,000, and so forth, is the basis for most of the strategies students adopt for whole number operations. Students' computational algorithms and procedures depend on knowing how to decompose numbers and knowing the effects of operating with multiples of 10. For example, one of the most common algorithms for addition is adding by place. Each number is decomposed into ones, tens, hundreds, and so forth; these parts are then combined. For example,

$326 + 493$

$300 + 400 = 700$

$20 + 90 = 110$

$6 + 3 = 9$

$700 + 110 + 9 = 819$

To carry out this algorithm fluently, students must know a great deal about place value, not just how to decompose numbers. They must also be able to apply their knowledge of single-digit sums such as $3 + 4$ and $2 + 9$ to sums such as $300 + 400$ and $20 + 90$. In other words, they know how to interpret the place value of numbers *as they operate with them*—in this case, that just as 2 ones plus 9 ones equals 11 ones, 2 tens plus 9 tens equals 11 tens, or 110.

As with addition, algorithms for multidigit multiplication also depend on knowing how the place value of numbers is interpreted as numbers are multiplied. Again, students must understand how they can apply knowledge of single-digit combinations such as 3×4 to solve problems such as 36×42.

For example,

36×42

$30 \times 40 = 1{,}200$

$30 \times 2 = 60$

$6 \times 40 = 240$

$6 \times 2 = 12$

$1{,}200 + 240 + 60 + 12 = 1{,}512$

Students gradually learn how a knowledge of 3×4 helps them solve 30×4, 3×40, 30×40, 3×400, and so forth.

Building Computational Fluency Over Time

There is a tremendous amount of work to do in the area of numbers and operations in Grades K–5.

- Kindergartners and first graders are still working on coordinating written and spoken numbers with their quantitative meaning.

- Second graders are uncovering the relationship between 10 ones and 1 ten and between 10 tens and 1 hundred.

- Third graders are immersed in how the properties of multiplication differ from the properties of addition.

- Fourth and fifth graders are solving multidigit problems and becoming flexible in their use of a number of algorithms.

This list provides only a brief glimpse of how much work there is to do in these grades.

Students gain computational fluency in each operation through several years of careful development. Extended time across several grades is spent on each operation. Students build computational fluency with small numbers as they learn about the meaning and properties of the operation.

Then they gradually expand their work to more difficult problems as they develop, analyze, compare, and practice general methods.

Let's use subtraction as an example of this process:

- In Kindergarten and Grade 1, students solve subtraction problems by modeling the action of subtraction.

- By Grade 2, students are articulating and using the inverse relationship between addition and subtraction to solve problems like the following: "If I have 10 cookies, how many more cookies do I need to bake so I have 24?"

- During Grades 2 and 3, students become fluent with the subtraction "facts" and model and solve a variety of types of subtraction problems, including comparison and missing part problems. By Grade 3, as students' understanding of the base-ten number system grows, they use their understanding of place value to solve problems with larger numbers.

- In Grades 3 and 4, students articulate, represent, and justify important generalizations about subtraction. For example, if you add the same amount to (or subtract it from) each number in a subtraction expression, the difference does not change, as in the equation $483 - 197 = 486 - 200$. In these grades, students also choose one or two procedures, practice them, and expand their command of these procedures with multidigit numbers.

- In Grades 4 and 5, as their fluency with subtraction increases, students analyze and compare strategies for solving subtraction problems. Because they are fluent with more "transparent" algorithms for subtraction in which the place value of the numbers is clear, they are now in a position to appreciate the shortcut notation of the U.S. traditional regrouping algorithm for subtraction, analyze how it works, and compare it to other algorithms. (See the Teacher Note, Computational Algorithms and Methods.)

This account gives only a glimpse of the work involved in understanding subtraction across the grades. Each operation has a similar complexity. It is critical that the time and depth required for the careful development of ideas is devoted to this strand. For this reason, in each of Grades 1–4, there are four units spread throughout the year that focus on whole numbers, operations, and the base-ten number system. In Kindergarten, three units focus on counting, quantity, and modeling addition and subtraction. In Grade 5, because of the increased emphasis on rational numbers, three units focus on whole numbers and two units focus on fractions, decimals, and percents. The whole number units within each grade build on each other in a careful sequence.

As you work with your students on whole number computation, here are some questions to keep in mind as you assess their progress toward computational fluency [adapted from Russell, 2000, p. 158]:

- Do students know and draw on basic facts and other number relationships?

- Do students use and understand the structure of the base-ten number system? For example, do students know the result of adding 100 to 2,340 or multiplying 40×500?

- Do students recognize related problems that can help with the problem?

- Do students use relationships among operations?

- Do students know what each number and numeral in the problem means (including subproblems)?

- Can students explain why the steps being used actually work?

- Do students have a clear way to record and keep track of their procedures?

- Do students have more than one approach for solving problems in each operation? Can they determine which problems lend themselves to different methods?

Supporting Computational Fluency Across the Curriculum

Work in the other content areas also connects to and supports the work on computational fluency in the number and operations units. For example, an emphasis on the foundations of algebra across the grades opens up important opportunities to strengthen work with numbers and operations. Within the number and operations units themselves, articulation, representation, and justification of general claims about the operations (an aspect of early algebraic thinking) strengthen students' understanding of the operations (see the Teacher Note, Foundations of Algebra in the Elementary Grades, and the Algebra Connections essay in each of the number and operations units). The work with functions provides interesting problem contexts in which students' work on ratio and on constant rates of change connect to and support their work on multiplication (see the Teacher Note, Foundations of Algebra in the Elementary Grades, and the Algebra Connections essay in each of the patterns, functions, and change units). Geometry and measurement units also provide contexts in which students revisit multiplication. Finally, the Classroom Routines (in Grades K–3) and Ten-Minute Math (in Grades 3–5) provide ongoing, regular practice of estimation and computation.

Reference

Russell, S. J. (2000). Developing computational fluency with whole numbers. *Teaching Children Mathematics 7*, 154–158.

Computational Algorithms and Methods

In the elementary grades, a central part of students' work is learning about addition, subtraction, multiplication, and division and becoming fluent and flexible in solving whole number computation problems. In the *Investigations* curriculum, students use methods and algorithms in which they can see clearly the steps of their solution and focus on the mathematical sense of what they are doing. They use and compare several different methods to deepen their understanding of the properties of the operations and to develop flexibility in solving problems. They practice methods for each operation so that they can use them efficiently to solve problems.

What Is an Algorithm?

An algorithm is a series of well-defined steps used to solve a certain class of problem (for example, all addition problems). Often, the sequence of steps is repeated with successive parts of the problem. For example, here is an example of an addition algorithm:

$$249 + 674$$

$$200 + 600 = 800$$

$$40 + 70 = 110$$

$$9 + 4 = 13$$

$$800 + 110 + 13 = 923$$

Written instructions for this algorithm might begin as follows:

1. Find the left-most place represented in the addends and add all the amounts in that place.

2. Move one place to the right and add all the amounts in that place in all the addends.

3. Repeat step 2 until all parts of all addends have been added.

4. Add the sums of each place.

To specify these instructions, as if we were going to teach them to a computer, we would have more work to do to make them even more specific and precise. For example, how is step 4 carried out? Should each place be added separately again and then combined? In practice, when students and adults use this algorithm, the partial sums that must be added in step 4 are generally easy enough to add mentally, as they are in this problem, although occasionally one might again break up some of the numbers.

Algorithms like this one, once understood and practiced, are general methods that can be used for a whole class of problems. The adding by place algorithm, for example, can be generalized for use with any addition problem. As students' knowledge of the number system expands, they learn to apply this algorithm to, for example, larger numbers or to decimals. Students also learn how to use clear and concise notation, to carry out some steps mentally, and to record those intermediate steps needed so that they can keep track of the solution process.

Nonalgorithmic Methods for Computing with Whole Numbers

Students also learn methods for computing with whole numbers that are not algorithmic—that is, one cannot completely specify the steps for carrying them out, and they do not generally involve a repetition of steps. However, these methods are studied because they are useful for solving certain problems. In thinking through why and how they work, students also deepen their understanding of the properties of the various operations. This work provides opportunities for students to articulate generalizations about the operations and to represent and justify them.

For example, here is one method a third grader might use to solve this problem:

$$\$7.46 + \$3.28 = \$7.50 + \$3.24 = \$10.74$$

The student changed the addition expression to an equivalent expression with numbers that made it easier to find the sum mentally. First graders often use this idea as they learn some of their addition combinations, transforming a combination they are learning into an equivalent combination they already know: $7 + 5 = 6 + 6 = 12$.

When students try to use the same method to make a subtraction problem easier to solve, they find that they must modify their method to create an equivalent problem. Instead of adding an amount to one number and subtracting it from the other, as in addition, they must add the same amount to (or subtract it from) each number:

$$182 - 69 = 183 - 70 = 113$$

Throughout the *Investigations* curriculum, methods like these are introduced and studied to deepen students' understanding of how these operations work and to engage them in proving their ideas using representations of the operations.

Because the ways in which a problem might be changed to make an equivalent problem that is easier to solve can vary (although it might be possible to precisely specify a particular variant of one of these methods), these methods are not algorithms. Students do not generally use such methods to solve a whole class of problems (e.g., any addition problem); rather, students who are flexible in their understanding of numbers and operations use finding equivalent expressions as one possible method and notice when a problem lends itself to solving in this way.

Learning Algorithms Across the Grades

In *Investigations,* students develop, use, and compare algorithms and other methods. These are not "invented" but are constructed with teacher support, as students' understanding of the operations and the base-ten number system grow (see the Teacher Note, Computational Fluency and Place Value). Because the algorithms that students learn are so grounded in knowledge of the operation and the number system, most of them arise naturally as students progress from single-digit to multidigit problems. For example, the adding by place addition algorithm shown earlier naturally grows out of what students are learning about how a number such as 24 is composed of 2 tens and 4 ones. It is part of the teacher's role to make these methods explicit, help students understand and practice them, and support students to gradually use more efficient methods. For example, a second grader who is adding on one number in parts might solve $49 + 34$ by adding on 10, then another 10, then another 10, then 4 to 49 ($49 + 10 + 10 + 10 + 4$). By having this student compare solutions with another student's whose first step is $49 + 30$, the teacher helps the first student analyze what is the same and different about their solutions and opens up the possibility for the first student of a more efficient method—adding on a multiple of 10 all at once rather than breaking it into 10s.

The algorithms and other methods that students learn about and use in *Investigations* for multidigit problems are characterized by their *transparency*. Transparent algorithms

• make the properties of the operations visible.

• show the place value of the numbers in the problem.

• make clear how a problem is broken into subproblems and how the results of these subproblems are recombined.

These characteristics are critical for students while they are learning the meaning of the operations and are building their understanding of the base-ten system. Here is an example of a transparent multiplication algorithm that might be used by a fourth grader:

$$
\begin{array}{r}
34 \\
\times\ 78 \\
\hline
2100 \\
280 \\
240 \\
\underline{32} \\
\end{array}
$$

$$2{,}000 + 500 + 150 + 2 = 2{,}652$$

In this algorithm, students record all numbers fully, showing the place value of all the digits. Because the result of each multiplication is shown, the application of the distributive property is kept track of clearly.

There is a misperception that many different algorithms might arise in a single classroom and that this multitude of algorithms will be confusing. In fact, there are only a few basic algorithms and methods for each operation that arise from students' work and that are emphasized in the curriculum. Each is tied closely to how students solve problems and to the basic characteristics and properties of the operation. Teacher Notes throughout the curriculum provide more detail about these methods.

Students can and do develop efficiency and fluency with these more transparent algorithms. As they do, they do some steps mentally and may no longer need to write out every step to keep track of their work. For example, in using the adding by place algorithm to add $249 + 674$, a competent user might simply jot down 800, 110, 13, and then add those partial sums mentally and record the answer. There may be times when you require students to write out their complete solution method so that you can see how they are solving problems, but for everyday use, efficient users of such algorithms will record only the steps they need.

These algorithms and methods are studied, compared, and analyzed for different reasons. All of them are transparent, preserve place value, and make visible important properties such as distributivity. Some can be practiced and provide general, efficient methods. Others are useful only for particular problems but are studied because of what they illuminate about the operations.

Studying the U.S. Standard Algorithms

The U.S. standard algorithms for addition, subtraction, and multiplication are also explicitly studied in *Investigations* but only after students are fully grounded in understanding the operation and using transparent algorithms for multidigit computation. These algorithms were developed for efficiency and compactness for handwritten computation. When these algorithms are used as a primary teaching tool, their very compactness, which can be an advantage for experienced users, becomes a disadvantage for young learners because they obscure the place value of the numbers and the properties of the operation.

Some students do use the standard algorithms with understanding. As these algorithms come up in class, they should be incorporated into the list of class strategies. Teachers should make sure that students who use them understand what the shortcut notation represents and that they can explain why these algorithms make sense. They should also know and understand other methods. In Grade 4, students revisit the U.S. standard addition algorithm formally, analyze how and why it works, and compare it to other algorithms they are using. In Grade 5, students revisit the U.S. standard subtraction and multiplication algorithms in the same way. Division methods studied in this curriculum focus on the inverse relationship between multiplication and division.

Teacher Note

Representations and Contexts for Mathematical Work

Mathematics involves describing and analyzing all kinds of mathematical relationships. Throughout the *Investigations* curriculum, students use representations and contexts to help them visualize these mathematical relationships. Thinking with representations and contexts allows students to express and further develop their ideas and enables students to engage with each other's ideas. Whether solving a multiplication problem, finding the area of a rectangle, describing the relationship between two variables, or ordering fractions, students use representations and contexts to investigate and explain.

The *Investigations* curriculum introduces a limited number of carefully chosen representations and contexts because they provide representations of mathematical relationships that students can use to solve problems and/or to show their ideas and solutions to others. Students may first use representations or contexts concretely, drawing or modeling with materials. Later, they incorporate these representations and contexts into mental models that they can call on to visualize the structure of problems and their solutions. Students develop the habit of making drawings, building models, and using representations to think with and to explain their thinking to others. They develop a repertoire of representations that they know well and can apply when faced with unfamiliar problem situations.

Good contexts and representations have the following characteristics:

- They are useful for a whole class of problems (e.g., addition problems).

- They can be extended to accommodate more complex problems and/or students' expanding repertoire of numbers.

- They do not overwhelm or interfere with the focus on mathematical content.

- Their structure embodies important characteristics of the mathematical relationships.

This Teacher Note provides some examples of how models, materials, and contexts are used by students across the grades.

Representations

Basic representations in the *Investigations* curriculum include connecting cubes, the 100 chart (and its variants, the 300, 1,000, and 10,000 charts), number lines, arrays, and sets of two-dimensional (2-D) and three-dimensional (3-D) shapes. Each representation provides access to certain characteristics, actions, and properties of numbers and operations or of geometric properties and relationships. Here are two examples.

Connecting Cubes

Connecting cubes are a basic material for counting and for modeling addition and subtraction in Grades K–2. The cubes are a discrete model of whole numbers and provide a uniform counting material for representing ones. Because they connect, they can be organized into sticks of ten cubes so that students can use them to represent tens and ones.

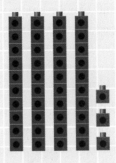

The individual cubes are visible in the connected stick of ten, so students can visualize how this stick represents the equivalence of 1 ten and 10 ones and then how 10 ten-sticks is equivalent to 1 hundred and 100 ones. Connecting cubes are a flexible material. They are well suited for modeling the basic actions of joining and separating. They can also be used to construct rectangular arrays for studying multiplication and area. Students also use the cubes to construct rectangular prisms and to analyze and visualize how the volume of the shape consists of a certain number of layers, each of which has the same dimensions.

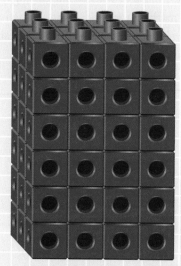

Each layer is 3 × 4. There are six layers.

The Number Line

The number line is another key representation of numbers. This continuous representation offers students another view of the number sequence and number relationships. Students' beginning work with number lines involves number lines that are already marked with the counting numbers.

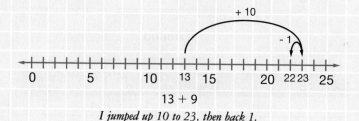

13 + 9
I jumped up 10 to 23, then back 1.

Later, students choose the part of the number line they need and which points on it should be marked as they use it to solve problems.

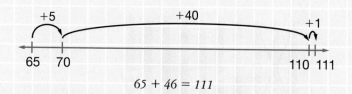

65 + 46 = 111

The number line provides access to the idea that numbers are infinite. At first, students come to this idea in relation to the counting sequence of whole numbers. Later, as they encounter negative numbers, they consider how the number line extends in both directions, that both positive and negative numbers "go on forever." In their study of rational numbers, they use the number line to model fractions and decimal fractions and consider how the segments of the number line between two successive whole numbers can be divided into smaller and smaller pieces. In later years, they will come to understand that there are an infinite number of numbers between any two successive integers.

For students to use a representation well, they need enough experience with it so that they understand its basic characteristics and can then use it themselves to model and solve problems. For example, using an unmarked number line flexibly requires that students have enough prior experience using the marked number line to count, add, and subtract.

Using Different Representations

Different representations offer different models of the mathematics and access to different mathematical ideas. For example, both place value models and number lines are useful in students' study of subtraction, but they each allow students to see different aspects of subtraction. A student solving the problem 103 − 37 might think about subtracting 37 in parts by visualizing a place value model of the numbers, subtracting 3 tens and then 7 ones (which, for ease of subtraction from 103, the student might split into 3 + 4).

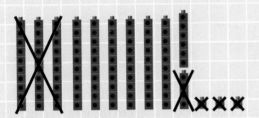

Another student might think about creating an easier, equivalent problem: $103 - 37 = 106 - 40$. This student might visualize "sliding" the interval from 37 to 103 along a number line to determine how to change the numbers, while preserving the difference between them.

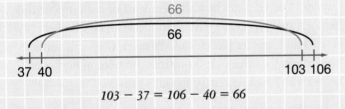

$$103 - 37 = 106 - 40 = 66$$

More details about these and other representations are provided throughout the curriculum units.

Contexts

Contexts and stories are also used to represent mathematical relationships. A good context can be created from familiar events or fantasy. Contexts that students can imagine and visualize give them access to ways of thinking about the mathematical ideas and relationships they are studying. For a context to be useful, it must be connected enough to students' experience that students can imagine and represent the actions and relationships. At the same time, the details of the context need not be elaborate, so that the nonmathematical aspects of the context stay in the background. Here are two examples.

The Penny Jar

One of the contexts in the patterns and functions units in Grades 1 and 4 is the Penny Jar. The Penny Jar contains some number of pennies (the starting amount) and then has a certain number of pennies added to it each day or with each round (the constant rate of change). This is one of the contexts used to engage students in exploring a function—the relationship of the number of days to the total number of pennies—that involves a constant rate of change. Students' knowledge of similar real-world contexts engages students quickly in the mathematics and helps them visualize the mathematical relationships, but it is not so elaborate that it obscures or distracts from the mathematics.

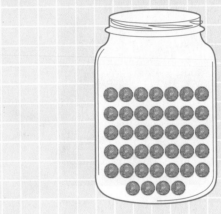

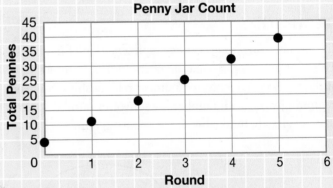

Number of Rounds	Total Number of Pennies
Start	4
1	11
2	18
3	25
4	32
5	39

Once students are familiar with the Penny Jar context, they can represent it in multiple ways, using pictures, tables, and graphs, to describe and analyze the relationship between the two variables.

Travel Stories

In Grade 3, travel stories are used as a context for subtraction. Students are familiar with taking trips by car or bus or have encountered such trips in stories or movies. They know about a trip having a starting point, an ending point, and a certain distance traveled. They are also familiar with stopping along the way for a meal or to take a break and with discussing how much of the distance has been covered and how much is still ahead of them.

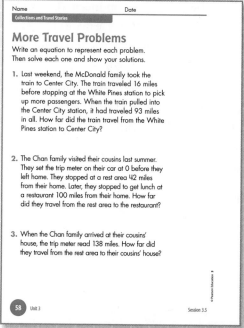

▲ Grade 3 Unit 3 *Student Activity Book,* page 58

Helping Students Connect to Contexts

Teachers often personalize these contexts for students to help them visualize and use it. For example, when using the Penny Jar context, one first-grade teacher had a brief discussion about places they or someone else they know used

to hold money and some reasons that money might get added to any of these. The teacher then referred to some of these situations as they discussed problems, "Let's say we're talking about Andre's situation when he is doing his chores. He has 3 pennies in the jar, and he is going to put in 2 pennies for each chore he completes." In using the travel story context, teachers also refer to situations that are familiar to students: "So let's say Janelle and her family are setting off to visit her grandma, like they did last summer, and the whole trip is 274 miles. ..."

More details about these and other contexts are provided throughout the curriculum units.

Using Representations and Contexts

Representations and contexts are central in mathematics at all levels for investigating, explaining, and justifying mathematical ideas. Students should move toward developing mental models of mathematical relationships that they call on routinely and will often use pictures, diagrams, and objects when they encounter new kinds of problems.

Students should use representations and contexts judiciously and with purpose. A first grader who is solving word problems that involve addition and subtraction might model every problem with cubes. Another student in the same class might model one or two problems; then, having visually confirmed the action of the operation, the student might solve the rest by imagining one quantity and counting on. A third student—or the same student later in the year—might reason about the numbers without using an image or model. In class discussions, both the teacher and students use representations to clarify and investigate mathematical ideas and to help all students focus on what is being discussed.

As a teacher, one of your roles is to support students in using representations and contexts and to help them develop mental images that they can call on. On the one hand, students need not show a picture for a problem when they have developed more efficient numerical tools and methods. For example, when one fourth grader was asked to solve a multiplication problem in two ways, he solved the problem by breaking it up efficiently, using the distributive property, and then showed a solution using groups of tally marks. His teacher let him know that using tally marks was not what she was looking for from him and reminded him of the work the class had been doing on changing one of the numbers in the problem and then adjusting the product.

On the other hand, students should understand that the use of representations and models is not a "crutch" in mathematics but is a powerful set of tools for investigating problem situations. In the classroom, encourage representation as a central part of mathematics activity. Make a habit of asking questions such as these:

- Is there a way you can show us your thinking using the number line or the 100 chart?

- Can you explain how your strategy makes sense using the travel context we have been using for some of the problems?

- You used a number line and Chris used a place-value sketch showing tens and ones. What is similar or different about these two approaches? Where can you see the four tens in Chris's place value sketch on Luc's number line solution?

- Karen, you are thinking of the multiplication problem as representing 47 classrooms with 23 students in each class. How did this context help you keep track of the parts of the problem?

- Can you show us with a picture or on the Geoboard what you mean when you say "a triangle is half of a rectangle"?

- What if you needed to explain or prove what you are saying to someone who came to visit our classroom? Is there a way you can show me why what you are saying is true with a picture or diagram?

When students are accustomed to incorporating representations in their daily mathematics work and considering what representations can be helpful for explaining mathematical ideas, they can also create their own images appropriate to a particular problem situation. Help students make these images simple enough so that they serve the mathematics rather than obscure it. The use of representations in class discussions helps illuminate students' ideas for each other and, by putting out an image that is available to all students, clarifies what mathematical relationships are being considered and invites more students into the conversation.

For further examples of students' use of representations, see the classroom stories in the section "Language and Representation" in Part 7, Working with the Range of Learners: Classroom Cases.

Teacher Note

Foundations of Algebra in the Elementary Grades

Algebra is a multifaceted area of mathematics content that has been described and classified in different ways. Across many of the classification schemes, four areas foundational to the study of algebra stand out: (1) generalizing and formalizing patterns; (2) representing and analyzing the structure of numbers and operations; (3) using symbolic notation to express functions and relations; and (4) representing and analyzing change.

In the *Investigations* curriculum, these areas of early algebra are addressed in two major ways: (1) work within the counting, number, and operations units focusing on generalizations that arise in the course of students' study of numbers and operations and (2) a coherent strand, consisting of one unit in each grade, K–5, that focuses on patterns, functions, and change. These two areas of emphasis are described here, followed by some additional information about the goals of work on early algebra in the curriculum.

Early Algebra: Making General Claims About Numbers and Operations

Each *Investigations* unit on counting, numbers, and operations includes a focus on reasoning and generalizing about numbers and operations. Even in beginning work with numbers and operations in Kindergarten and Grade 1, students are already noticing regularities about numbers and operations. For example, in the K–1 game *Double Compare,* each student in the pair selects two number cards. The student with the greater sum says "me." In this early work, before students know their single-digit addition combinations, most students are counting all or counting on to determine the sum. But consider how students are reasoning in the following brief episode:

> Bridget and Siva are playing *Double Compare.* Bridget draws a 5 and a 2; Siva draws a 5 and a 3 and immediately says "me," indicating that he has the

greater sum. Siva usually counts both amounts by ones to get the sum, so the teacher asks him, "How did you know you have more?" Siva responds, "Because I have a 3 and she has a 2, and 3 is bigger." Bridget is nodding vigorously and adds, "The 5s don't count."

How are the students in this episode figuring out who has the greater sum? Why does Siva only compare 3 with 2, and what does Bridget mean when she says the "5s don't count"? Implicit in these students' work is a general claim about adding numbers that many young students use: If you are comparing two addition expressions, and one of the addends in the first expression is the same as one of the addends in the second, then you need only compare the other two addends to determine which expression has the greater sum. This is a mouthful to put into words, and students might not be able to articulate this idea completely; nevertheless, they are reasoning based on this idea. In later years, this idea can be represented with symbolic notation:

For any numbers a, b, c, and d when $a = c$ and $b < d$, then $a + b < c + d$.

$a = c$	$b < d$	$a + b < c + d$
$5 = 5$	$2 < 3$	$5 + 2 < 5 + 3$

Part of the teaching work in the elementary grades is to help students articulate, represent, investigate, and justify such general claims that arise naturally in the course of their work with numbers and operations. In each of the number and operations units in Grades K–5, the Algebra Connections essay highlights several of these general ideas about properties and relationships relevant to the work in that curriculum unit, with examples of how students think about and represent them. Investigation and discussion of some of these generalizations are built into unit sessions; for others, Algebra Notes alert the teacher to activities or discussions in which these ideas are likely to arise and could be pursued.

In the course of articulating, representing, and justifying their ideas about such general claims, students in the elementary grades are beginning to engage in proving—a central part of mathematics. They consider the questions: Does this generalization apply to *all* numbers (in the domain under consideration, usually whole numbers)? Why does it work? How do you know? In two of the number and operations units in each grade, 2–5, you will find a Teacher Note that focuses on proof and justification. These Teacher Notes provide examples of the ways that students at that grade level engage in proving and how their proofs, based on representations, are related to the proofs a mathematician might carry out.

Examples of the general claims highlighted in the curriculum in Grades K–2 are as follows:

- Counting the same set of objects in different orders results in the same count.

- If one number is larger than another, and the same number is added to each, the first total will be larger than the second: $3 + 5 > 2 + 5$.

- You can add two numbers in either order: $6 + 3 = 3 + 6$.

- If you add an amount to one addend and subtract it from another addend, the sum remains the same: $6 + 6 = 12$; $7 + 5 = 12$.

- Addition and subtraction are related. If adding two numbers gives a certain sum, then subtracting one of the addends from the sum results in the other addend: $6 + 7 = 13$; $13 - 7 = 6$; $13 - 6 = 7$.

- You can break numbers into parts to add them: $6 + 8 = 6 + (4 + 4) = (6 + 4) + 4$.

- If you add two even numbers, the sum is even. If you add two odd numbers, the sum is even. If you add an even number and an odd number, the sum is odd.

Some of the generalizations investigated in Grades K–2 are revisited in Grades 3–5 with higher numbers and more complex problems. In addition, new general claims are investigated. Examples of general claims highlighted in Grades 3–5 are as follows:

- If you add the same amount to both numbers in a subtraction problem, the difference does not change: $145 - 97 = 148 - 100$.

- You can multiply two numbers in either order: $32 \times 20 = 20 \times 32$.

- You can break numbers into parts to multiply them, but each part of each number must be multiplied by each part of the other number: $7 \times 24 = 7 \times (20 + 4) = (7 \times 20) + (7 \times 4)$.

- Multiplication and division are related. If multiplying two numbers gives a certain product, then dividing that product by one of the original factors results in the other factor: $9 \times 8 = 72$; $72 \div 8 = 9$; $72 \div 9 = 8$.

- A factor of a number is a factor of multiples of that number: 3 is a factor of 15; 15 is a factor of 30, so 3 is a factor of 30.

- If you double (or triple) one of the factors in a multiplication problem and halve (or third) the other, the product remains the same: $164 \times 4 = 328 \times 2$.

Early Algebra: Patterns, Functions, and Change

Investigations includes a coherent K–5 strand on patterns, functions, and change, with one unit in each grade. The content of these units starts with repeating patterns and number sequences in Grades K and 1, connects these patterns and sequences to functional relationships beginning in Grade 2, and then develops ideas about linear and nonlinear contexts that involve relationships between two variables in Grades 3–5. In each of these units in K–5, the Algebra Connections essay highlights some of the ideas students work on in that unit, and how they connect to later work in algebra.

Patterns and Functions in Grades K–2

Work with repeating patterns has long been a staple of mathematics work in the primary grades, but it often seems to have little connection to work in later grades. In the *Investigations* sequence, students' study of the structure of repeating patterns is connected to work with ratios and linear functions by associating the repeating pattern with the counting numbers. Consider this example:

> Students have been building repeating color patterns using connecting cubes. This red-blue-green repeating pattern has been numbered with the counting numbers, starting with 1. Students are considering which numbers are associated with the green cubes:

1 2 3 4 5 6 7 8 9 10 11 12

Kamala says that the greens have a "counting by 3s" pattern: 3, 6, 9, 12. Esperanza says, "it will always be on the threes because every time you skip two, then it's green." Theo adds, remembering a previous Investigation in which they built buildings from connecting cubes with the same number of cubes in each layer: "It's like the same pattern we made when we made the building. It's always adding threes. One floor is three, two floors is six, and you keep adding three— 3, 6, 9, um, 12, and you keep going by 3s."

Students are recognizing the underlying 1:3 ratio in both situations. In the repeating pattern, there is a relationship between the position of each green cube among all green cubes and its position among all the cubes: the *first* green is in position 3 in the sequence, the *second* green in position 6, the *third* green in position 9, and so forth. In the cube building, there are 3 cubes for each floor: one floor has

3 cubes, 2 floors have 6 cubes, 3 floors have 9 cubes, and so forth. These constant ratio situations are students' first examples of linear change—change at a constant rate.

Examples of ideas investigated in Grades K–2 in these units are as follows:

- Repeating patterns can be described as iterations of a unit. This repeating color pattern can be divided into its units, the part that repeats:

- When the elements of a repeating pattern are numbered with the counting numbers, elements in the pattern can be characterized by a particular number sequence. In a red-blue-red-blue connecting cube train, the blue cubes are numbered 2, 4, 6, 8, . . . , and the red cubes are numbered 1, 3, 5, 7, ...

1   3   5   7   9   11
  2   4   6   8   10   12

- The same number sequence can represent different situations. The blue cubes in a red-blue repeating pattern and the claps in a tap-clap repeating pattern fall in the same numbered positions.

- In a ratio situation, as one quantity changes by a certain amount, the other quantity always changes by a certain amount (for each day, there are 3 pennies added to the jar).

- Tables are a representation that can be used to show how one variable changes in relation to another.

- The same ratio relationship can occur in different contexts (e.g., 3 pennies per day, 3 cubes per "floor").

Patterns, Functions, and Change in Grades 3–5

In Grades 3–5, students focus on both linear and nonlinear change. Students study situations with a constant rate of change, in which two variables are related in ways that can be expressed in a verbal rule or an equation (such as the relationship between the total number of pennies in a jar and the number of days pennies have been collected, when a fixed number of pennies is added to the jar each day). They learn to take into account any starting amount (i.e., the number of pennies in the jar at the beginning) and the rate of change (i.e., the number of pennies added to the jar each day). They also study relationships in which the value of one variable cannot be determined based on the value of the other (such as the relationship between temperature and time in Grade 3 and between plant growth and time in Grade 4). In Grades 4 and 5, they also encounter situations in which the relationship between the two variables can be determined, but the change is not occurring at a constant rate, for example, a Penny Jar in which the number of pennies doubles each day.

Students work extensively with ways of representing relationships between two variables: with words, with tables and graphs, with numbers, and (starting in Grade 4) with symbolic notation. These units reinforce and connect with work in other units on multiplication, ratio, area, volume, and graphing. The Algebra Connections essay in each of the patterns, functions, and change units provides more detailed information about this sequence of students' work and how it connects to algebra.

Examples of ideas investigated in these units in Grades 3–5 (in addition to some of those in the K–2 list that continue to be studied in new contexts) are as follows:

- Line graphs are a representation that can show the relationship between two variables. A line graph represents both individual values of the variable and the rate of change of one variable in relation to another.

- In a situation with a constant rate of change, the value of one variable can be determined, given the value of the other.

- The relationship between two variables in a situation with a constant rate of change can be described in words and with symbolic notation.

- In some situations, the rate of change is determined but not constant. In these situations, the rate of change may be, for example, increasing by a constant amount.

Early Algebra Is Fundamental

Underlying the work in early algebra are, according to one of the *Investigations'* mathematician advisors, "foundational principles"—principles that connect elementary students' work in arithmetic to later work in algebra. For example, when second graders consider how changing the order of numbers in an addition or subtraction problem affects the sum or difference, they can engage in reasoning about foundational ideas, in this case, that addition is commutative, but subtraction is not: $a + b = b + a$, but $c - d \neq d - c$. Even though they may not yet have the experience with negative numbers to allow them to completely make sense of $14 - 26$, they see, through modeling and representing this problem, that it does not have the same difference as $26 - 14$. In later years, they will come to see that there *is* a regularity here, that if $c - d = a$, then $d - c = -a$, or $c - d = -(d - c)$.

Similarly, when fifth graders develop representations to show why halving one factor in a multiplication problem and doubling the other results in the same product, they are applying knowledge of foundational properties of multiplication and division. In later years, they may explain the more general claim that dividing one factor by any number (except 0) and multiplying the other factor by the same number maintains the same product by reference to the associative property of multiplication and to multiplication by 1—the identity element for multiplication. Through a series of steps, based on these properties of multiplication, one can show that, if a, b, and n are numbers $\left(n \neq 0 \right)$, then $a \times b = a \times b \times \frac{n}{n} = (a \times n) \times \left(\frac{b}{n} \right)$.

For most adults, notation such as the use of variables, operations, and equal signs is the chief identifying feature of algebra. Although students use symbolic notation in Grades 4 and 5, the notation is not the focus of activity in Grades K–5. Underlying the notation are ways of reasoning about how the operations work. This *reasoning* about how numbers can be put together and taken apart under different operations or about relationships between two changing quantities, *not* the notation, is the central work of elementary students in algebra.

Algebra for All Students

Work in early algebra in the elementary classroom has the potential of enhancing the learning of *all* students. The teachers with whom the *Investigations* team collaborated during the development of the curriculum commented on this potential in their classrooms. Teacher collaborators reported that students who tend to have difficulty in mathematics become stronger mathematical thinkers through this work. As one teacher wrote, "When I began to work on generalizations with my students, I noticed a shift in my less capable learners. Things seemed more accessible to them." When the generalizations are made explicit—through language and representations used to justify them—they become accessible to more students and can become the foundation for greater computational fluency. Furthermore, the disposition to create a representation when a mathematical question arises supports students in reasoning through their confusions.

At the same time, students who generally outperform their peers in mathematics find this content challenging and stimulating. The study of numbers and operations extends beyond efficient computation to the excitement of making and proving conjectures about mathematical relationships that apply to an infinite class of numbers. A teacher explained, "Students develop a habit of mind of looking beyond the activity to search for something more, some broader mathematical context to fit the experience into."

Early algebra is not an add-on. The foundations of algebra arise naturally throughout students' work with numbers, operations, and patterns and by using familiar and accessible contexts to investigate how one set of values changes in relation to another. This work anchors students' concepts of the operations and underlies greater computational flexibility.

Teacher Note

Discussing Mathematical Ideas

Throughout the *Investigations* curriculum, whole-class discussion is a key aspect of students' mathematical activity. Class discussion provides a time for students to

- articulate their mathematical ideas.

- share different approaches to solving a problem.

- identify and investigate what they don't understand.

- analyze why a solution works or how it is flawed.

- pose conjectures and identify evidence to support them.

- collaborate to build ideas or solve problems.

- develop mathematical language.

- use representations to describe mathematical relationships.

- compare and connect students' various ideas, representations, and solutions.

- learn to consider and question each other's ideas.

By carefully selecting problems, representations, and solutions for the whole class to consider, the teacher focuses discussion on key mathematical ideas and works with the class as a whole to move students' thinking forward.

Building a Mathematical Community

In the first weeks of school, teachers help the class develop norms for classroom discussion and work with students on attitudes and behavior that will support productive math discussions. Most teachers find that they need to work quite explicitly with students throughout the school year to first establish and then maintain expectations for class discussion. During discussions, teachers keep the flow of ideas organized and remind students about the appropriate focus. For example, "Right now I want comments that are either agreeing with, disagreeing with, or commenting on Yolanda's idea," or "So we now have three different approaches to this problem on the board. Is there a way in which Jill's is similar

to Corey's?" Teachers also find opportunities to comment directly on student actions, behavior, and contributions that support productive discourse:

> Because Stephen was willing to talk through what was confusing him when he got an answer that he knew wasn't right, it seemed to really help all of us understand this kind of problem better.

> When Kamala put up her picture of the problem, I heard some of you say, "Ooh!" What was it you understood when you saw that picture? Did anyone else have a picture or a diagram that helped you understand how to solve this problem?

And from time to time teachers discuss directly with the class what aspects of class discussions have been helping or hindering students' participation:

> What helps you be willing to share your work or make an observation during class discussion? Are there times you don't feel comfortable speaking? Why is that?

Building an inclusive mathematics classroom involves a focus on respect for student ideas and acceptance of differences. Working on establishing this community with students will vary across grades and even from one year to another, depending on the needs and experiences of your students. (See the section "Setting Up the Mathematical Community" in Part 7, Working with the Range of Learners: Classroom Cases for some teachers' thoughts on building the classroom mathematics community.)

Focusing Class Discussions

Students' ideas are important and are, in fact, central to discussion. But if a discussion bounces among too many different ideas or tries to include too many different approaches, the discussion becomes ungrounded and hard for students to follow. Simply listing one problem-solving approach after another doesn't engage students beyond the few moments when they are contributing their own idea.

The Math Focus Points for Discussion and sample teacher dialogue found in the text for every discussion will help you guide the discussion. In preparing for class, ask yourself:

- What do I want this discussion to accomplish?

- What do I want all students to take away from this discussion?

- How will the time spent as a whole class enhance the work students have done individually or in pairs or groups?

During work that precedes the discussion, observe students' work with the upcoming discussion in mind. Ask yourself:

- What is a difficulty that many students are having?

- What is a problem that many students are struggling with?

- Is there a question that one pair or group came up with that it would be fruitful for the whole class to discuss?

- What are the basic approaches to solving this problem that students are using?

- Which students or groups have ideas or approaches that should be shared?

Student Participation

Whole-class discussion time is precious class time; it should serve to consolidate or move ahead the math thinking of all students. Find ways during discussions to elicit responses from different students. Although all students may not participate in any one discussion, all of your students' voices should be heard over the course of several discussions. There are many ways to work with students to encourage them to participate. For example, listen carefully to students' ideas and look carefully at their work during activities. Help particular students prepare to share one of their ideas. At first, some students might be more comfortable if you put their solution, representation, or idea on the board or a

transparency and present it to the class yourself; alternatively, the student might explain a certain part of the solution, while you add to the student's explanation.

Think of ways to invite all students' participation during each discussion by asking students to raise hands if they used the same approach or if they agree or disagree with a statement you or another student makes. Pose a question and have students discuss it for a few minutes in pairs before having the whole class consider it. Use wait time judiciously and think about ways that students can use quiet signals when they are ready to respond (e.g., thumbs up rather than hands waving); then students who are still thinking are not distracted.

Ideas are bound to come up that you cannot pursue during class discussions. Sometimes you cannot follow or decipher a student's idea at the moment or you are not sure about how it relates to what is being discussed. If you don't understand what a student is saying, you might ask another student to interpret or talk to the student later. Don't be afraid to let students know that you have to think about something and get back to them or follow up with them after the discussion. You can always bring an idea back to the class later if you decide it would be important for the class to think about it.

You can find other ways to follow up on a student's idea that is not central or accessible for the whole class: "I was thinking about your idea, and here's a problem I thought you could try it on." Some teachers have a "parking lot" poster for ideas that come up during class but they don't have time to pursue. These ideas may come up again later or can be referred to when they become relevant. The better you know the curriculum, the more you will know when they might come up.

Setting Up the Classroom for Discussion

It is critical that students are sitting in such a way that everyone is focused on the discussion and everyone can hear. If there are representations that students need to see during the discussions, they must be large enough and dark enough so that everyone can see them.

A variety of seating arrangements for class discussions can work, as long as there are clear expectations connected to them. In some classrooms, students gather on a rug for the class meeting and then return to their places or choose places for work time. In other classrooms, students often stay at their own desks for meetings. Some teachers vary the setting, with students staying at their desks when the meeting will be short and gathering together when a longer time is needed.

To facilitate a smooth transition to meeting on the rug, some teachers assign students places to sit on the rug, changing them every month or so. Others place circles, mats, or white boards to clearly mark the places available for students to sit. Others allow students to sit wherever they want in a circle as long as they can see the teacher and all of the other students. They might remind students to make a good choice about sitting in a position and next to classmates that enables them to focus on the discussion. While some students can pay attention while sitting on the floor, others do better in a chair.

Guidelines for Whole-Class Discussions

In summary, here are some guidelines to keep in mind for your class's whole-group discussions:

- Set up norms and review them frequently; point out examples in which they are working.

- Plan a clear purpose and focus for each discussion, based on the listed Focus Points.

- Use wait time to give students time to think.

- Ask students to use quiet student signals to indicate they are ready to respond.

- Prepare with some students ahead of time to participate in the discussion.

- Have clear visuals that everyone can see and refer to.

- Establish a routine arrangement that ensures that everyone can hear and see.

- Select only a few students to share solutions.

When all students come to a discussion prepared to listen actively and to contribute ideas, the class discussions provide an important forum in which they can articulate, represent, connect, and consolidate the mathematical ideas they have been working on.

Racial and Linguistic Diversity in the Classroom: What Does Equity Mean in Today's Math Classroom?

… we have no patterns for relating across our human differences as equals. As a result, those differences have been misnamed and misused in the service of separation and confusion.[1]

Audre Lorde

We must not, in trying to think about how we can make a big difference, ignore the small daily differences we can make, which, over time, add up to big differences that we often cannot foresee.[2]

Marian Wright Edelman

U.S. public schools are responsible for educating students who are more racially and linguistically diverse than at any other time in our history. The beginning of the 21st century in the United States is marked by an influx of immigrants, and schools and teachers are at the front door meeting these students. Hence, many teachers work in classrooms with increasing numbers of immigrant students, students of color, and linguistically diverse students who often face unique challenges related to language proficiency, cultural and social adaptation, and poverty. What are the issues and challenges for teachers in these diverse classrooms?

While developing this curriculum, the *Investigations* staff and field-test teachers worked together to continue educating ourselves about this question. Many of us have had direct experience teaching in schools where students come from diverse racial, cultural, and linguistic backgrounds. In many cases, the students' culture, race, ethnicity, and first language are different from those of the teacher. This Teacher Note provides a glimpse into the complex issues about racial,

cultural, and linguistic diversity being discussed in the field of education today. It also provides resources for further reading, including those we found helpful in our own professional development.

Equity in the Mathematics Classroom

Equity does not mean that every student should receive identical instruction; instead, it demands that reasonable and appropriate accommodations be made as needed to promote access and attainment for all students. (NCTM, 2000, p. 11)

Investigations was developed with the assumption that all learners can engage in challenging and substantive mathematics. Assumptions about students' capacity and inclination to learn in school can undermine their access to and participation in significant mathematics learning. An extensive body of literature documents the persistence of these assumptions and their effects on students' opportunity to learn. For example, students of color and those whose first language is not English are often seen in terms of what they lack instead of what they bring to the learning environment (termed in the literature a *deficit thinking* model). Student underperformance in school may be explained by student and family shortcomings, behavior that does not match a particular set of norms, immaturity, or lack of intelligence. Students who do not speak fluent English may be judged as having poor or underdeveloped conceptual understanding because they cannot yet express the complexity of their thinking in English. Misunderstanding cultural differences can lead schools to inappropriately place children into special education and low-ability groups and to expect less from them than from other children. For instance, Entwistle and Alexander (1989) report that poor black children are often described as less mature, and, consequently, school personnel may hold lower expectations for them than for children whose socioeconomic status is higher.

---

[1] From a paper delivered at the Copeland Colloquium, Amherst College, in April, 1980. The paper was entitled, "Age, Race, Class, and Sex: Women Redefining Difference."

[2] Marian Wright Edelman, "Families in Peril: An Agenda for Social Change," The W. E. B. Du Bois Lectures (Cambridge, Mass.: Harvard University Press, 1987), p. 107.

Many teachers are working hard to improve learning opportunities for these students, with the goal of enhancing both the learning climate and students' educational performance. In this work, teachers must consider the broader issues as well as practices, procedures, strategies, and other key aspects of schooling. In an educational setting, equity indicates a state in which all children—students of color and white students, males and females, successful students and those who have fallen behind, and students who have been denied access in the past—have equal opportunities to learn, participate in challenging programs, and have equal access to the services they need to benefit from that education. Equity has sometimes been oversimplified to mean that all students should be treated the same—neutrally and without differentiation. Rather, differences matter, and matter in specific ways. Successful learning experiences depend on teachers building on the contributions of all students and recognizing the differences that matter to them.

In the mathematics education literature, researchers from four projects, three in the United States and one in South Africa, looked across their projects to identify features of classrooms "essential for supporting students' understanding" in mathematics (Hiebert et al., 1997). They organize these in five dimensions, one of which is "equity and accessibility." The authors describe this dimension as fundamental:

> [E]quity . . . is not an add-on or an optional dimension. It is an integral part of a system of instruction that sets students' understanding of mathematics as the goal. Without equity, the other dimensions are restricted and the system does not function well. (p. 12)

Race and Linguistic Diversity

While teaching a seminar on race in education several years ago, one of the authors of this essay was met with a remarkable silence and little open discussion of race, racism, and the ways they come up in classroom teaching. Some think that racism is no longer an issue in schools, and that "color blindness" is the way to approach a diverse class of students. However, many in the field believe that explicit classroom attention to race, ethnicity, and home language results in increased communication and learning.

Race (or ethnicity) can have overlapping and coexisting categories of meaning. Sometimes, race signifies being economically, socially, politically, and educationally oppressed. Other times it signifies a sense of community and belonging, involving valuable associations with a particular group, history, cultural codes, and sensibilities. Race conveys multiple meanings, and racism takes on multiple forms, subject to context and situation. Whether expressed subtly or with crude directness, the effects of racism are felt in everyday school experience. Preconceptions about who students are, which are based on surface behaviors, can mask important potential.

For example, in one classroom, a Hmong girl is quiet, well behaved, and does little to demand attention. But although she is well behaved, she is not engaged and does not quite know what's going on in the lesson. In another classroom, a young black boy is distracted and disruptive, eager to contribute, but often "in trouble." The Hmong girl might be seen as a model student—quiet, hard working, high achieving, and nonchallenging of classroom norms. In contrast, the black boy might be seen as loud, threatening, noncompliant, dysfunctional, and low achieving. The characterization of the Hmong girl seems positive, even flattering, in comparison to the characterization of the black boy. However, both views may be silencing the voices, needs, and potential contributions of these children in different ways. For the Hmong girl, a focus on seemingly compliant behavior may lead the teacher to ignore her educational needs. For the black boy, a focus on seemingly bad behavior may distract the teacher from recognizing his educational strengths.

To understand all students' experiences—to support them in rigorous learning and to respect the variety of their language practices, histories, and identities—educators must continue to learn about the issues of race and racism, cultural and linguistic diversity, and teaching practices and strategies that support the learning of all students.

Teaching Practices and Strategies

Many important insights about teaching practices and strategies that support students of color and English language learners can be gleaned from those who have been studying and writing in the field. Some of these educators and researchers focus specifically on the mathematics classroom, but there are also accounts from science and literacy that have a great deal to offer the teaching of mathematics.

Gloria Ladson-Billings studied exemplary teachers of African-American students and has written about an approach of "culturally relevant teaching." Although the teachers she studied differed in the way they structured their classrooms—some appeared more "traditional," while others were more "progressive" in their teaching strategies—their conceptions of and beliefs about teaching and learning had many commonalities. Here is a subset of characteristics of these teachers adapted from Ladson-Billings' list (1995). These teachers:

• believed that all students are capable of academic success.

• saw their pedagogy as always in process.

• developed a community of learners.

• encouraged students to learn collaboratively and be responsible for each other.

• believed that knowledge is shared, recycled, and constructed.

• believed they themselves must be passionate about learning.

• believed they must scaffold, or build bridges, to facilitate learning.

• believed assessment must be multifaceted.

Overall, these teachers supported their students and held them to high standards:

> Students were not permitted to choose failure in their classrooms. They cajoled, nagged, pestered, and bribed

the students to work at high intellectual levels. Absent from their discourse was the "language of lacking." . . . Instead, teachers talked about their own shortcomings and limitations and ways they needed to change to ensure student success. (p. 479)

Critical to teaching students who bring a variety of cultural, social, and linguistic experience into the classroom is what Marilyn Cochran-Smith (1995b) calls "understanding children's understanding":

> [C]entral to learning to teach in a culturally and linguistically diverse society is understanding children's understanding or exploring what it means to know a child, to consider his or her background, behaviors, and interactions with others, and to try to do what Duckworth calls "give reason" to the ways the child constructs meanings and interpretations, drawing on experiences and knowledge developed both inside and outside the classroom. (p. 511)

Eleanor Duckworth, whom Cochran-Smith cites above, may have originated the phrase *understanding children's understanding* in her essay of the same name (1996). In that essay, she discusses the idea of "giving children reason" as she describes a group of teachers in a study group who set themselves this challenge: "[E]very time a child did or said something whose meaning was not immediately obvious . . . [they] sought to understand the way in which . . . [it] could be construed to make sense" (pp. 86–87).

This work of hearing and understanding students' ideas, discourse, and representations and involving all of them in significant intellectual work can be especially challenging when students come from backgrounds quite different from the teacher's own. Cindy Ballenger's *Teaching Other People's Children* (1999) and Vivian Paley's *White Teacher* (1989) provide first-person accounts of teachers who are actively examining their own preconceptions about the behavior and discourse of the students they teach. Ballenger expresses how her initial belief that all students could learn was not enough:

I began with these children expecting deficits, not because I believed they or their background was deficient—I was definitely against such a view—but because I did not know how to see their strengths . . . I came to see . . . strengths . . . that are part of an intellectual tradition, not always a schooled tradition, but an intellectual one nonetheless, and one that, therefore, had a great deal to say to teaching and learning. (p. 3)

Ballenger recounts her journey in learning to listen to the sense of her students, both "honoring the child's home discourse" and engaging the student in "school-based and discipline-based ways of talking, acting, and knowing" (p. 6).

Working in English with students whose first language is not English presents two challenges to teachers who do not share the student's first language: (1) how to learn about, respect, and support the discourse practices that students can contribute from their own knowledge and communities; and (2) how to bring students into the language of the discipline of mathematics in English. Judit Moschkovich (1999) identifies two critical functions of mathematical discussions for English language learners: "uncovering the mathematical content in student contributions and bringing different ways of talking and points of view into contact" (p. 11). She identifies several important instructional strategies that support these students' participation in math discussions (p. 11):

• using several expressions for the same concept

• using gestures and objects to clarify meaning

• accepting and building on student responses

• revoicing student statements with more technical terms

• focusing not only on vocabulary development but also on mathematical content and argumentation practices

Josiane Hudicourt-Barnes (2003) writes about the participation of students whose home language is Haitian Creole. Her research highlights the way that understanding the forms of discourse students contribute from their own culture enables teachers to uncover and appreciate how students are making sense of subject matter. Although she writes about science learning, her observations are applicable to the mathematics classroom: "To be 'responsive to the children and responsible to the subject matter' (Ball, 1997, p. 776), we must be able to hear children's diverse voices and create opportunities for them to pursue their ideas and questions (p. 17)." Further, she argues that classroom discourse that follows a rigid, restrictive format "may mean that children from families of non-Western traditions are shut out of classroom participation and that skills from other traditions are devalued and subtracted from children's cognitive repertoires, and therefore also made unavailable to their fellow students" (p. 17).

Being "responsive to the children and responsive to the subject matter" is highlighted by many of the writers in this field. They emphasize that the teacher's responsibility is *both* to the students' ideas, sense making, and forms of discourse *and* to bringing these students in to the ideas, vocabulary, and ways of working in the discipline of the content area. Gloria Ladson-Billings (2002) sums up her observations of a teacher whose urban, largely African American, students, initially hated writing:

> To meet the academic goals he had set, Carter had to rethink his practice in some fundamental ways. . . . He had to keep a sense of uncertainty and a willingness to question in the forefront of his teaching. . . . while Carter empathized with the students' struggle to write he understood that his job was to teach them to do it. He didn't put them down for not enjoying writing or writing well, but he also did not let them off the hook. He had to help them appreciate the power and fulfillment of writing and he had to preserve each student's sense of self. (p. 118)

Continuing to Learn

Continuing to learn is something we all can do. This Teacher Note attempts only to introduce you to some authors and resources who can contribute to that learning. Many of the resources cited here include rich examples from classrooms that can evoke productive interaction when read and discussed with peers. You may have opportunities to take advantage of courses, seminars, or study groups, such as the one that Lawrence and Tatum (1997) describe, or to self-organize peer discussions of articles in the field.

Teachers can also pose their own questions and study their own classrooms. Writing brief case studies in which you raise your own questions about these issues in your teaching and then sharing your writing can be a rich source of learning. You might start by reading what other teachers have written about their own practice as they reflect on their teaching of diverse students. For example, in *What's Happening in Math Class?* (Schifter, 1996), Alissa Sheinbach writes about three students who are struggling in mathematics (vol. 1, pp. 115–129), Allen Gagnon writes about his Spanish-speaking students (vol. 1, pp. 129–136), and Nora Toney recounts her own experiences with racism as a student (when she was bused into a largely white school) and later as a teacher herself (vol. 2, pp. 26–36). After describing some successful experiences in mathematics she had as an adult that contrasted with her experience in the "low group" as a student, Toney concludes by identifying factors that have been important to her own learning:

> I have discovered the ingredients necessary for me to learn and achieve success: high teacher expectation, fairness, inclusiveness, engaging contextual material, constant monitoring and feedback, discussions/debates, and reflective writing. Generally speaking, I need numerous opportunities to connect my thinking and ideas to new concepts and ideas. These factors facilitated my *learning* of mathematics, so now I am trying to incorporate these same factors into *teaching* mathematics. (p. 36)

References and Additional Readings

Ball, D. (1997). What do students know? Facing challenges of distance, context, and desire in trying to hear children. In T. Biddle, T. Good, & I. Goodson (Eds.), *International handbook on teachers and teaching* (pp. 769–817). Dordrecht, Netherlands: Kluwer Press.

Ballenger, C. (1999). *Teaching other people's children: Literacy and learning in a bilingual classroom.* New York: Teachers College Press.

Cochran-Smith, M. (1995a). Uncertain allies: Understanding the boundaries of race and teaching. *Harvard Educational Review, 63,* 541–570.

Cochran-Smith, M. (1995b). Color blindness and basket making are not the answers: Confronting the dilemmas of race, culture, and language diversity in teacher education. *American Educational Research Journal, 32,* 493–522.

Duckworth, E. (1996). *"The having of wonderful ideas" and other essays on teaching and learning.* New York: Teachers College Press.

Entwistle, D., and Alexander, K. (1989). Early schooling as a "critical period" phenomenon. In K. Namboodiri & R. Corwin (Eds.), *Research in Sociology of Education and Socialization,* Volume 8, (pp. 27–55) Greenwich, CT: Jai Press.

Heath, S. B. (1983). *Ways with words: Language, life, and work in communities and classrooms.* New York: Cambridge University Press.

Hiebert, J., Carpenter, T. P., Fennema, E., Fuson, K. C., Wearne, D., Murray, H., et al. (1997). *Making sense: Teaching and learning mathematics with understanding.* Portsmouth, NH: Heinemann.

Hudicourt-Barnes, J. (2003). The use of argumentation in Haitian Creole science classrooms. *Harvard Educational Review, 73*(1), 73–93.

King, J. (1991). Dysconscious racism: Ideology, identity, and the miseducation of teachers. *The Journal of Negro Education, 60,* 133–146.

Ladson-Billings, G. (1994). *The dreamkeepers: Successful teaching for African American students.* San Francisco: Jossey-Bass.

Ladson-Billings, G. (1995). Toward a theory of culturally relevant pedagogy. *American Educational Research Journal, 32,* 465–491.

Ladson-Billings, G. (2002). I ain't writin' nuttin': Permission to fail and demands to succeed in urban classrooms. In L. Delpit & J. K. Dowdy (Eds.), *The skin that we speak: Thoughts on language and culture in the classroom* (pp. 107–120). New York: The New Press.

Lawrence, S. M., & Tatum, B. D. (1997). White educators as allies: Moving from awareness to action. In M. Fine, L. Weis, L. C. Powell, & L. M. Wong (Eds.), *Off white: Readings on race, power, and society* (pp. 333–342). New York: Routledge.

Lewis, A. (2003). *Race in the schoolyard: Negotiating the color line in classrooms and communities.* New Brunswick, New Jersey and London: Rutgers University Press.

Moschkovich, J. (1999). Supporting the participation of English language learners in mathematical discussions. *For the Learning of Mathematics,* 19(1), 11–19.

National Council of Teachers of Mathematics. (2000). *Principles and standards for school mathematics.* Reston, VA: Author.

Obidah, J., & Teel, K. M. (1996). The impact of race on cultural differences on the teacher/student relationship: A collaborative classroom study by an African American and Caucasian teacher research team. *Kansas Association for Supervision and Curriculum Development Record,* 14, 70–86.

Obidah, J., & Teel, K. M. (2001). *Because of the kids.* New York: Teachers College Press.

Paley, V. G. (1989). *White teacher.* Cambridge, MA: Harvard University Press.

Schifter, D. (1996). *What's happening in math class? Vol. 1: Envisioning new practices through teacher narratives ; Vol. 2: Reconstructing professional identities.* New York: Teachers College Press.

Titles of Grade 1 Teacher Notes by Unit

PART 7

Working with the Range of Learners

Preview

All teachers are faced with the challenge of meeting the needs of a range of learners in their classrooms. The range of learners can include students who struggle in certain areas of mathematics, those who excel in math, students who are English Language Learners, and students who have particular learning needs.

This section contains a series of case studies written by first-grade teachers from urban, suburban, and rural schools, telling how they implemented the *Investigations* program in their classrooms. The students in these classrooms vary on many dimensions, including gender, language, culture and ethnicity, and special needs. They present a range of strengths and needs in their prior experience with mathematics and their confidence in the classroom.

Through their writing, these teachers bring us into their classrooms and invite us to participate in how they think about supporting their range of learners. As they captured moments in time in their classrooms, the teachers did not intend to provide exemplary actions to be emulated or a how-to manual of what to do for particular students or with particular activities. Rather, they offer the kind of thinking teachers do as a matter of course in their teaching. Through the hundreds of interactions they have with their students each day, teachers try to understand what those students bring to their learning and how to support them in moving further. In these case studies, they share some of that thinking.

We collected these cases together in this book, rather than including them with the curriculum units, because they are not designed to illustrate "how to do" a particular activity. Rather, as a group, they provide examples and questions to inspire your own questioning and reflection. You may want to use this set of cases on your own or discuss them with a group of colleagues.

Keep in mind that each case provides only a glimpse into a teacher's classroom. Just as you would not expect anyone to understand the complexity of the issues you face in your own classroom from such a brief glimpse, the cases cannot provide all the background information you might need to understand a particular teacher's decision with a particular student on a particular day. But you do not need to know more detail to use these cases for your own professional development. Use them as starting points when considering similar issues that you face with your students. The questions at the end of each case provide a starting point for discussion. If you discuss these cases with colleagues in a cross-grade group, you will have even more examples to consider by combining the sets of cases from two or more grades.

The classroom cases are grouped into three themes, focusing on some of the most important issues teachers face as they work to meet the needs of their students. In the first section, "Setting Up the Mathematical Community," teachers write about how they create a supportive and productive learning environment in their classrooms. In the second section, "Accommodations for Learning," teachers focus on specific modifications they make to meet the needs of some of their learners. Because these teachers chose to write about particular students in their classrooms, the cases do not cover all the kinds of needs and accommodations you might encounter. However, even though the specific students discussed may differ from students in your own classroom, these teachers consistently found that accommodations they had made for one student often spilled over to benefit other students with related needs. In the last section, "Language and Representation," teachers share how they help students use representations and develop language to investigate and express mathematical ideas.

There is, of course, much overlap. Some cases illustrate ideas that could fall into more than one of these sections. You will find ideas from one section cropping up in the cases in other sections. For example, when teachers develop accommodations for learning, they are often using mathematical representations or helping students connect their language to the mathematical ideas.

Note: Pseudonyms have been used for all student and teacher names.

Summary of Cases

Setting Up the Mathematical Community

Building the Math Community: Setting Norms for Discussions

Leah Schultz expects all of her students to participate in mathematical conversations and shares how she provides them the skills to be able to do so.

Modeling, Molding, and Maintaining the Classroom Community

Carly Fredericks shares how she builds and maintains the mathematical community and focuses on how she supports the range of learners in her classroom as they solve story problems.

Accommodations for Learning

Learning How to Count

This is the first of three cases written by Anita Martinez, which follow Alicia as she learns to count.

Let's Keep on Counting: Finding Patterns in the Number Sequence

In part two of the series, Anita Martinez works with Alicia as she learns which multiple of 10 comes after numbers ending in 9 in the number sequence up to 50.

What Comes After 49?

In the last case in the series, Anita Martinez interviews Alicia to find out what she has learned about counting during the year.

Marbles and Blocks: *How Many of Each?*

Laura McCann finds a way to make *How Many of Each?* problems more accessible for some of her learners.

Challenging Highly Competent Learners

Gretchen Harris shares how she provides challenging activities for some of her students who show great competence in mathematics.

Crayon Puzzles

Carly Fredericks reflects on two students who represent the wide spectrum of what students do while solving *Crayon Puzzles* and the challenges that spectrum raises for effective teaching.

Language and Representation

How Many of Each? Probing Student Understanding

Laura McCann works with Kim to help her connect visual and numeric representations as she decomposes numbers in *How Many of Each?* and *Today's Number* problems.

Who Is Talking? Reflections on a Discussion

Laura McCann reflects on a classroom discussion and notices that some of her students are participating more than others.

Seeing Connections: A First Grader Compares Representations of Number Sequences

Gretchen Harris shares an interesting connection a student made between the Staircase Tower problems and the Penny Jar problems.

How Many More? Understanding Through Sharing and Discussion

Maria Lopez found that providing her students time to share their strategies for solving comparison problems helped them make sense of the problems, clarify their thinking, and become more comfortable with the mathematics.

Setting Up the Mathematical Community

Building the Math Community: Setting Norms for Discussions

Creating a classroom culture that allows all students to share ideas, listen to, and learn from each other takes a lot of thought and work on the part of the teacher. Since these skills and practices develop over time, the first month of school is a time when teachers begin to establish the classroom atmosphere that they would like to see unfold throughout the year. An important component in developing an inclusive community is helping all students learn to participate in mathematics discussions, including those who don't feel confident about their math skills and those who opt to stay on the periphery.

During the first weeks of school, Leah Schultz, who teaches in a Grades 1–2 combination classroom, puts particular effort into communicating her expectation that everyone participates and shares ideas in math discussions and providing all her students with the elements they need to do so successfully.

Before I can talk with my students about what makes a good math discussion, they need to have some idea of what mathematics discussions will look and sound like. They must have some experiences on which to base their ideas. Consequently, I feel that students need to experience a good discussion before they can articulate what makes a good discussion.

I begin by making my expectations clear through my actions and words as we learn the basic mathematics routines of the classroom. For example, I expect that "everyone can and *should* participate in the math we do as a group." In the morning during *Calendar,* we have a routine that helps the students think about breaking a number into two parts. I make a cube train to represent the day's date, so if today is the 12th, I have a train of 12 cubes. I break off some and put them behind my back. The class counts how many cubes are still showing and tries to figure out how many are behind my back.

I have a multiage class, so when I teach this routine, the second graders who were in my class last year already know what to do. On our first days of this routine, I noticed that some of the new first graders were participating. Others were not, perhaps because they were not sure how to do it, because it was hard for them to pay attention, or because they already had the idea that they couldn't or didn't need to.

I made sure during those initial discussions that we shared strategies that all students could understand. In the beginning, the students most eager to share were the ones who knew what to do and got an answer easily. For instance, when no one talked about counting on their fingers or using the calendar to count, I specifically asked if anyone used those strategies. This question was an important one because several of my younger and more struggling students could use this strategy as a way into the math problems. I found getting this strategy into the conversation helped make the mathematics accessible.

In the next days when there were students still opting out of the sharing activity, I let my expectation be known by saying:

I know that *everybody* can figure out how many cubes are behind my back. Some people might count on their fingers; some people might use the calendar or a number fact that they know. I am going to wait for everyone to have an answer, so use a quiet ready sign to let me know that you have an answer.

Then I waited. Most of the students gave me the "thumb up" quiet ready sign, but there were a few students who, I could tell, had not engaged in the activity. I politely asked one student if he was ready and he said "No." I told him, again politely, that we would wait. "We'll wait until everyone has had enough time." Since almost everyone was eager to share, they waited patiently. I cannot stress enough that this process was not a punitive one. Rather, by waiting, I was modeling for students the importance of waiting until each person had a strategy for solving the problem.

I watched myself and realized that in these first few weeks, I try to make it clear that we are a mathematics community that includes everybody. When I say that I want everybody to engage in a problem and then give time to solve it, *I really do mean that everybody can solve it.* It is not easy to get that across to the struggling learners in the room who often do not include themselves in the group that can "do it." I find myself working hard to let students know I expect them to find an answer without putting too much pressure on them or singling them out.

Some students are surprised when I wait for their answer. They are already expecting that they cannot do what others do, so they remove themselves from the expectations and are surprised when I plunk them right back into the group. Others feel discomfort and hope that I will forget them again so that they can slink back to the shadows. Over time, they realize that I will not, and they begin to rise to the occasion. I always accompany my expectation with strategies that make the math accessible to them. It is a two-sided deal: "You make sure you try to participate, and I will make sure that I give you the tools to do so." I want the students to know that our math discussions require all our voices. So when I say, "Whom haven't we heard from yet?" it lets the students know that I don't want any voices missing from our discussions.

Later, we will have an explicit conversation about what makes a good math discussion. For now, we have these initial experiences that will enable students to have that discussion in the near future.

Ms. Schultz finds that being explicit about her expectations that all students participate in classroom discussions must be accompanied by actions that convey how serious she is about this commitment. She carefully builds experiences of participation among all her students so that everyone can feel and be an active member of the math community. If students can see themselves as contributing members of the community, they will continue to participate. If students exclude themselves, for whatever reason, and the teacher does not actively work to bring them into the conversation, they will continue to exclude themselves.

Questions for Discussion

1. **What are the specific strategies that Ms. Schultz uses to make her expectations for class discussions explicit? What does she do to help her less experienced students, particularly the first graders who still rely on less developed counting strategies, feel confident about participating in these discussions?**

2. **In your class, how do you communicate through words and actions your expectation that everyone should participate? How do you help the least confident students develop and share their ideas?**

Modeling, Molding, and Maintaining the Classroom Community

Carly Fredericks has two goals in mind as she begins the school year. The first is to get to know each of her first graders so as to foster and support the learning of each student throughout the year. Her second goal is to create a classroom community where students are able to learn and work together. These goals are closely related, and Ms. Fredericks recognizes that achieving them takes time. In this case, Ms. Fredericks shares how she lays the groundwork for creating a positive and supportive learning environment that is responsive to the needs of each learner and how she builds on that foundation throughout the year.

It is important to take time at the beginning of the school year to establish routines and expectations that help to build a safe and, hopefully, exciting environment for learning. Regardless of whether the focus is literacy, science, social studies, or math, my goal is to support each student's own journey. I have come to realize that establishing a community that recognizes and meets the needs of each individual and fosters understanding of the subject matter takes time and needs to be modeled, molded, and maintained from the first day of school until the last.

Early in the school year, I focus on a number of things: putting routines in place for where to find and how to use materials, establishing guidelines for following a schedule, organizing work, and establishing expectations for student work and behavior. In some ways these are tangible stepping-stones in building our community. The more I focus on their importance early in the year, the stronger our foundation as a class. The students and I work together to learn how to navigate the classroom and the curriculum. While exploring materials, learning new games, and diving into new investigations, students are simultaneously learning how to work together and how to learn from and with each other.

Before too long my focus shifts to thinking about how students are engaging with the mathematics and with each other. There is a great deal of emphasis on how to work together when playing a game or working side by side on the same or similar problems. In the early stages, I move around the classroom and listen for ways students talk with each other. Initially, I hear comments such as, "No, it's my turn," or "I don't think that's how you play." I recognize that my students are trying to negotiate a number of things at once: how to play, the mathematics being highlighted in the game, and the interpersonal dynamics of playing competitively or cooperatively with a classmate. For some students, one or more of these essential elements fall into place easily. Others struggle each step along the way.

I have found it helpful to share some of the conversations I hear with the whole class. Often to end Math Workshop, but sometimes even during, I bring the students back together to share what I have observed. Sometimes this is focused on a mathematical strategy. For example,

I noticed that when Tim and Marney were playing *Double Compare,* Tim counted the pictures on only one of his cards. Tim, can you tell us more about this strategy?

Other times I might focus on the ways the students talk to each other.

I heard Rae and Siobhan encourage each other. Rae noticed that Siobhan had different solutions to the problem than she did. I heard Rae say, "Siobhan, my answer is different. How did you get that?"

Sharing the students' actual language, successes, and confusions helps all of us learn.

I begin Math Workshop in different ways—sometimes by focusing on the mathematics, sometimes by teaching a new game or about new kinds of problems to solve, and other times by focusing on organizational skills. After several years of work with this curriculum, I know where organizational skills can become problematic. For example, for many of my students, it is initially difficult to deal with all of the different kinds of story problems. They seem to do well keeping track of game pieces and rules, but when it comes to tackling word problems, many seem to be all over the place. I have tried several different ways to organize this work for students. I have thought about how much room they need on a page and how many problems they can solve during one session.

I have also needed to address the readability of each problem. For many of my first graders, once they get the gist of a problem type, they are able to read similar problems on their own. For others, both the oral and written language is too complex. When I first started using the curriculum, I didn't really focus on this and became frustrated when the students were not working independently. My first resolution was to read the problems orally, but this did not last long, because each student works at a different level of mathematical understanding, speed, and confidence. Therefore, I decided to pair students and match them to problems, just as I match texts and students in reading. I realize that it is often *not* the mathematics that is difficult; it is the amount of reading required and the skills it takes to organize and communicate solutions. Pairing students guarantees that all students have access to the work and are not hindered by their inability to read a problem.

As we encounter story problems in the curriculum, I keep a list of students based on various criteria, including how independent they are with the task at hand. I try to assess whether my students are able to make sense of the mathematics. For example, in a *How Many of Each?* type problem, I know that for some students the number being targeted is not too big or too small but well within their range. For other students, I know I can adjust the number in the problem to make it more challenging or more manageable. In thinking about the mathematics in the problem, I also have to make sure that my students understand the language. We use class discussions to highlight specific words such as *more* and *less* and phrases like *"How many more?"* Asking the class to talk about these ideas is important and gives us a basis for other kinds of discussions that focus more on strategies. In fact, part of any strategy is figuring out what the problem is asking.

Finally, I check in to see if my students are making sense of the problem. For students who are moving quickly through the work, I consider additional options for when they are finished. With students for whom the work is just right, not too easy or too hard, I focus on making sure the environment in the classroom is conducive to them building confidence and skill. I know what these students need most is uninterrupted time to focus and practice. I want to make sure that they have enough time and the materials they need to work efficiently. They also need ways to feel safe when asking questions, showing frustrations, and sharing enthusiasm about successes and new understandings.

For students who are struggling, I work more on helping them understand the language used in a given problem. I have realized that it is easy to take for granted that my students comprehend such concepts as *more, less,* and *how many.* At times I set up alternative choices to let them work specifically on understanding *one* of these concepts.

Throughout the year, looking for ways to group my students effectively and differentiate the curriculum when needed has been very important and contributes to the success of all my students.

In this case, Ms. Fredericks illustrates the many components involved in building a strong classroom community. To begin with, she introduces her students to a variety of classroom routines to familiarize them with how the classroom is organized and provide them with a safe way to begin to work together. Next, through modeling and sharing, she helps her students learn how to work together in a positive and supportive way. Finally, Ms. Fredericks assesses the individual needs of each of her learners and thinks about how she can best meet their needs through partnering, individualized instruction, or specific accommodations. In this way, Ms. Fredericks is able to create a positive work environment that is supportive of the range of learners in her classroom.

Questions for Discussion

1. In this case, Ms. Fredericks writes that establishing a community is a process that needs to be modeled, molded, and maintained from the first day of school until the last. Can you find examples of how Ms. Fredericks models, molds, and maintains the classroom community?

2. Ms. Fredericks writes specifically about the challenges that word problems pose to first graders. What are the issues that she identifies? What steps does she take to make word problems accessible to all of her students?

3. Early in the school year, what do you focus on when creating a mathematical community? What structures do you put in place early on to support the range of learners in your mathematics classroom?

Accommodations for Learning

Learning How to Count

Anita Martinez teaches in a two-way-bilingual Grade 1 classroom. In this setting, native English speakers and native Spanish speakers receive instruction in both languages, with the goal being that all students develop fluency and literacy in both languages. In this case, Ms. Martinez focuses on one student, Alicia, who enters school with number concepts that are not as well developed as those of her peers. At the beginning of the school year, Alicia cannot reliably count a group of objects between 10 and 20. Ms. Martinez wants Alicia not only to learn the number sequence but to reflect on her thinking as well. As Ms. Martinez describes, her goal is for Alicia to "have ownership of her learning."

One of the first activities in first grade is a counting activity. Students make a design with 20 pattern blocks and prove that they have 20. As Alicia worked, I observed her get more than 20 blocks, so I asked her if she had 20, fewer than 20, or more than 20. With great confidence she said she had more than 20. I asked her to show me. As she began to count, she forgot what number she said last, went back, skipped numbers, or double-counted the same block. Alicia seemed upset and tried again. As I left to observe other students, I had a general sense that one-to-one correspondence and the oral counting sequence were not yet clear for Alicia.

A few days later Alicia picked this same activity during Math Workshop. I wanted to see what she would do a second time. She had 16 blocks on the table. I stopped her and asked her how many blocks she had so far. She began to count and skipped a few blocks, ending up with a count of 13. I asked her whether she was sure, so she counted again. This time she counted 16. I asked her whether it could be 13 one time and 16 another time. She laughed and slapped her forehead with her hand to indicate she had made a mistake. She went back to counting and came up with 16 again. She was convinced that there were 16 blocks.

Teacher: How do you know?

Alicia: I counted.

Teacher: You counted 13 before, so how can you be sure it is 16?

Alicia: Because I counted.

Teacher: Do you have more or less than 20?

Alicia wasn't sure and smiled again.

On several occasions, I talked with all the students about the common mistakes they made, such as skipping numbers when counting, not counting each object, or counting the same object more than once. Although I couldn't tell whether Alicia followed our conversations, her work showed that she did. The daily routines *Start With/Get To* and *Morning Meeting: Attendance* also helped with her counting. I had posted the number line on the wall, and Alicia used it frequently whenever she was counting out loud or working at her table. The classroom environment and routines provided Alicia with resources she could use to have ownership of her learning.

Alicia began checking her counting every time. She was incorporating into her counting what we had discussed in the whole class as well as in our brief exchanges. I realized how powerful it had been for Alicia to reflect on her work. She was not only learning the number sequence but also important skills involved in counting. On the mid-year assessment, Alicia showed confidence and accuracy with both counting and solving problems requiring counting.

Even though Alicia could not count accurately, Ms. Martinez engaged her as a thinker and asked her to reflect on her actions ("How do you know?") and to consider inconsistencies in her reasoning ("You counted 13 before, so how can you be sure it is 16?") Ms. Martinez persisted throughout the next months with Alicia, asking her to describe how she was counting and to double-check her count. Alicia was able to internalize the math routines of the class and make use of the available resources, such as the number line. Gradually, Alicia not only learned how to count but also became aware of the importance of checking her work, an important skill she can apply throughout her math work.

Questions for Discussion

1. What did Alicia already know about numbers? What confused her?

2. What strategies did Ms. Martinez use to help Alicia reflect on her work to build understanding?

3. What might be the next steps for Alicia or students like her?

Let's Keep on Counting: Finding Patterns in the Number Sequence

Alicia is a first grader who entered school with number concepts that were not as well developed as those of her peers. During the first months of school, her teacher, Ms. Martinez, engaged her in activities that allowed Alicia to learn how to reliably count a set of up to 20 objects. In this case, Ms. Martinez works with Alicia on the number sequence up to 50. She noticed that Alicia can use her knowledge of counting from 1 to 9 to count from 21 to 29, 31 to 39, and so forth, but Alicia does not know what numbers follow 29, 39, 49, and so on. Ms. Martinez is aware that this difficulty is common among students who are learning to count, and once again involves Alicia in thinking about her mistakes.

As I was writing a long strip of numbers up to 100 in preparation for our math session, Alicia sat next to me to help me out. I took this opportunity to see how much she knew or had incorporated from our classroom discussions. As I wrote 49, she said "20" for the next number. She knows that after 49, you don't say "forty ten" (she has already made that mistake before and could correct herself now). She knows that something with "ty" comes next, but she doesn't know which number with "ty" to say.

My students have been working with the 100 chart, playing *Missing Numbers.* There have been several class discussions about how you know what numbers come after certain numbers (e.g., "What comes after 39?" "What comes after 43?"). Many students have been identifying patterns on the 100 chart, but Alicia, while she enjoyed the activity of guessing, was not noticing the regularities in the number sequence.

After several days of working on the 100 chart, I called Alicia over to my table and asked her to count how many chips there were in a container. As she took them out one by one, she counted correctly from 1 to 15. She paused but didn't forget where she was, as she would have in September, and continued "16, 17, 18, 19, 30." I didn't stop her. She kept counting with a clear sequence from 31 to 39. At that point, she looked at me for help, but I didn't answer.

Alicia: Fifty!! No? Yes?

Teacher: No or yes?

Alicia: No, because it is 20, and I made a mistake—21, 22, 23, 24, 25, 26, 27, 28, 29, 30, 31.

As she counted, she neatly took one chip with each count.

Teacher: I am curious about something. When you began to count, you said "19, 30." Then you kept counting and you said "29, 30." Does 30 come after 19 or after 29?

Alicia: After 29 because look [she starts counting all over again], 1, 2, 3, 4, . . ., 9, 10, 11, 12, . . ., 19, 20, 21, 22, . . ., 29, 30.

Teacher: Oh! So after 29 comes 30. And how do you know it?

Alicia: Because it sounds good. The words sound good: 31, 32, 33, 34, . . ., 39, 50!

Teacher: Alicia, you told me that after 19 comes 20 [I wrote these two numbers], and that after 29 comes 30 [I wrote these], then you said that after 39 comes 50. What do you think?

We were running out of time, and Alicia couldn't tell me what about it sounded good. Was it the sounds of the numbers in the sequence? Was it something else? Now my goal is to help Alicia find patterns in the number sequence to 50.

Having spent a few months with Alicia, I am confident that she will eventually be able to make sense of what the other students are saying about the patterns in the number sequence to 100. As long as I continue these math conversations and engage Alicia in work around the 100 chart, she will internalize some of these ideas. I also think that my interactions with her, in which I present her

mistakes as points of reflection, will help her figure out a solution to her problems. I am aware that the classroom environment is supporting her struggles and providing her with tools to figure out how the number system works. She might respond later than the other students, but for me, it is her individual progress that matters.

Although Alicia is struggling with ideas about counting that other students in the class have mastered more easily, Ms. Martinez persists in working with her over a long period of time, asking questions that focus Alicia's attention on what is problematic in her thinking—counting one object with every counting word in September and noticing the regularities of the counting sequence above 19 in February. Ms. Martinez interacts with Alicia as a learner and thinker, not as a student who is failing. She has a clear mathematical agenda for Alicia and pursues it.

Questions for Discussion

1. What did Alicia already know about the number system?

2. What questions did Ms. Martinez pose? How did these questions help Alicia move forward in her understanding? What learning opportunities did the variety of tools and representations that Ms. Martinez offered present to Alicia?

3. What additional experiences might you provide for Alicia or other students like her?

What Comes After 49?

In this case, Ms. Martinez concentrates once again on Alicia. In September, Alicia could not maintain one-to-one correspondence when counting a collection of up to 20 objects. In February, she was struggling with the multiples of 10 in the number sequence up to 50. The other students in Alicia's class had been studying the number sequence up to 100, and over the months they had many conversations about patterns in the number sequence. However, Ms. Martinez wasn't convinced that Alicia followed the content of those conversations and wanted to learn, through an informal interview, what she understood. Ms. Martinez asked Alicia to count how many chips there were in a container, just as she had done in February. In this way she was able to assess Alicia's growth over time.

As she took one chip at a time, Alicia began counting, "1, 2, 3, . . ., 16, 18, 20." She noticed she had made a mistake and went back, "16, 17, 18, 20," she went back again, "18, 19, 20" and confidently continued up to 49, after which she said 30. Alicia continued, "31, 32, . . ., 39, 30." She stopped. She was puzzled. Since I had been taking notes of what she said, she looked at my notes and exclaimed: "Not again! Thirty cannot come again!" as she pointed at all the 30s on my paper.

Teacher: What makes you say that?

Alicia: No, it can't because it is a number. You only need one number. If it comes again, it is wrong.

I understood her expression "you only need one number" as meaning there is only a single 30 in a collection; the numbers are all different, so you say one number only once in the sequence. I decided not to ask for further clarification. I thought she had said as much as she could, and I did not want to distract her from the counting.

Teacher: So what can you do?

Alicia began counting one by one with her fingers from 1 to 50 without making any mistakes. This time I was interested in pushing her further, so I asked:

Teacher: How do you know it is 50?

I wrote 47, 48, 49, 50 on the paper because I had the impression that the visual support helped her think.

Alicia: Because all of these are 4s and then comes 5.

And she kept writing the numbers up to 60.

Teacher: How do you know it is 60?

Alicia: Because all of these have a 5 and then comes 6.

I decided to give her a new number and ask her what comes next. I wrote 66. She wrote 65.

Teacher: So we count 66, 65?

Alicia: "No, it is a 7."

She wrote 67 and continued the sequence up to 70.

Teacher: What comes after 79?

At first she said 68, but she wrote 80. She corrected herself and kept writing the number sequence up to 90.

As I looked back at what Alicia did in February and compared it to what she was doing in May, I identified areas of progress and as well as new difficulties. In February, Alicia had difficulties counting past 20, and she needed my help to notice her mistakes. Now, in May, Alicia identifies some of those mistakes by herself and knows how to correct them. When I asked her in February for some elaboration on the idea of what number came after a number ending in 9, she had no way to figure it out by herself. She could check on the number line but couldn't come up with the number by herself because she had no understanding of the patterns in the number system. Now, in May, Alicia is beginning to explain those patterns. She knows that after the 40s come the 50s "because all of these are 4s and then comes 5."

Despite her progress, I need to remind myself that knowing the number sequence does not mean a student has a sense of quantity or understands what the digits in the numbers represent. And this is probably true for many of my students. So there is more work ahead. I also need to make sure that Alicia knows how to match a written number with an oral number.

Alicia continues to have some difficulties with counting, but I am very excited about her progress and her interest in learning. She needs more support from me than the other students do, but she is definitely moving forward.

Ms. Martinez has worked with Alicia throughout the year to help her become a thinker and an independent learner. Ms. Martinez worked with Alicia's mistakes as entry points for learning and in that process helped Alicia to monitor her work, an essential skill when doing math.

Ms. Martinez had established high standards for Alicia, and she continues to formulate important goals while working with Alicia. She has trust in Alicia as a learner, and Alicia has demonstrated that she can learn.

Questions for Discussion

1. What strengths does Alicia show in this case?

2. How does Ms. Martinez help Alicia recognize her mistakes? How does she probe Alicia's thinking?

3. What might be the specific next steps for Alicia or students like her to build understanding?

Marbles and Blocks: *How Many of Each?*

In this case, Laura McCann's first-grade students are working on solving a How Many of Each? *problem involving blocks and marbles. Realizing that modeling this type of problem has proven to be difficult for some of her students in the past, Ms. McCann works to make the problems more accessible for some of her learners.*

As my class shifts from geometry back to numbers and operations, I hear some enthusiasm from the students. We begin with the *How Many of Each?* problem concerning 9 toys. I remind the students that some of the toys are blocks, and some of the toys are marbles.

As I observe the class during the introductory discussion, I notice that some students seem ready to begin and appear to remember these problems from our last number unit. Others seem a little foggy but start to nod with understanding as the conversation continues. But I also spy a group of students who seem unsure of this assignment. I remember that these are the same students who had some difficulty with these problems the last time around. In thinking back to some of the mistakes they had previously made when solving these problems—like adding 9 blocks and 9 marbles to get 18 instead of finding a combination of blocks and marbles with a total of 9—I realize that these students need more structured support for solving this type of problem. I have an idea of where I can begin with them today.

While the class begins working, I notice that Courtney and Jasmine are tapping their pencils and looking around the room. I decide to bring over some egg cartons and pattern blocks to help them work through the problem. While the girls tell me what they know about the problem, I quickly resize the egg cartons so each carton has only 9 cups. From their explanation of the problem, I can tell that the girls seem to understand that there are some blocks and some marbles, but they cannot be more specific about how to determine how many of each object there could be.

I begin by asking them how they can use the pattern blocks as visual models. The girls quickly decide that hexagons will represent the marbles because they have a roundish shape, and the squares will be the blocks because they resemble blocks. Next, I introduce the egg cartons and point out that these trays will hold exactly 9 toys. I explain that their job will be to fill each cup with one toy. After they have filled the tray, they must count how many blocks they used and then how many marbles.

Courtney immediately fills the tray with 9 hexagons and says, "9." I commend her for following directions but then explain that in the context of this problem there are definitely some of each, so there must be at least 1 block in the mix. She takes out 1 hexagon and refills the cup with a square. She then counts the totals of each, and I ask her to show these amounts on her paper.

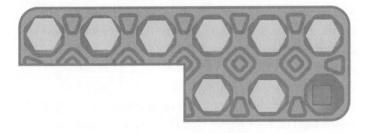

Jasmine, who is sitting next to her, seems to understand how to use this new tool with a little less scaffolding and has already come up with a possibility.

I leave the girls and begin to circulate around the room to check in on the other students. I am quickly approached by two boys, Edward and Peter, who tell me they are finished and have found every solution. I ask them to record their strategy on the back of their paper and emphasize that I want them to explain how they know they have found every solution. I look at Edward's paper and see that he has two columns—one column labeled "Blocks" and one labeled "Marbles"—and that he started with 1 block and 8 marbles. I notice that each time he subtracted one from the marbles column he added it to the blocks column.

Edward's Strategy:

Blocks	Marbles
1	8
2	7
3	6
4	5
5	4
6	3
7	2
8	1

I decide to check back in with Jasmine and Courtney. I notice that Jasmine is now finding solutions without using the egg carton. It seems that the initial structuring helped her to visualize the task, and she is now able to work without it. I see that Courtney is still using the egg carton to help her. She has chosen to fill the eggcups in a pattern—hexagon, square, hexagon, square, hexagon, square, hexagon, square, hexagon, so I know that she is not yet ready to think about approaching this problem systematically in the way that Edward and Peter can. However, she is working on the important idea of breaking up a quantity into two parts in different ways.

Finally, it is time to share. I call on Courtney first as I know she has only a few to share, and I would like to give her an opportunity early on. I call on several other students early on for this same reason. I call on students with every, or almost every, solution later on so that I can observe them scan their sheets to see if they can pick out a solution we have not previously recorded. When we have all of the solutions, I ask the students to share how they know we have all of the solutions. I know that Courtney, and perhaps Jasmine, have not thought about this question. Their level of reasoning is still emerging, and this conversation could be beyond their reach, but I feel that it is important for them to be part of it just the same.

Jonathan raises his hand to share that he knows we have them all because he remembers from our previous work on these problems that every number leading up to the total will be used once by each item. He has written at the bottom of his paper:

$$\cancel{1}\ \cancel{2}\ \cancel{3}\ \cancel{4}\ \cancel{5}\ \cancel{6}\ \cancel{7}\ \cancel{8}$$

Each number is slashed out as a sort of checklist that he used for the number of marbles and the number of blocks. When I ask why he didn't include the numbers 9 or 0, he confidently replied that because the problem said there were some of each, there has to be at least one marble or block and therefore 9 and 0 cannot be part of the solution.

Jane shares next. Her conjecture is that she knows we have all the solutions because we have eight solutions recorded, and that the number of solutions will be one less than the total number of items. I take a minute to work this through in my head; is she right? I tell her that I am intrigued by this thinking and am wondering if some of my mathematicians will check out her theory with other numbers. It will be a worthwhile discussion to come back to, but I am running out of time and cannot digress right now. It is Scott who ultimately shares the approach that I saw Edward use earlier. Scott also adds one to each column while subtracting one from the other column.

As Scott explains his strategy, I see some students nodding in recognition, and I realize that they are the ones who have solved the problem the same way. In an attempt to help some of my other students understand this approach, I grab a box of counters and a box of Geoblocks. I line up 8 counters in a row and tell the students that the counters represent the marbles. I then place 1 Geoblock down to represent the blocks. Next, I demonstrate how by removing one "marble" at a time and replacing it with a block, we can see Sam's strategy happening.

I hope that these accommodations have added depth to our work on this type of problem. I know I will not have to wait long to find out!

Knowing that visualizing the structure of whole and parts in How Many of Each? *problems is difficult for some of her students, Ms. McCann finds ways to make the problems more accessible. She provides some of her learners with tools so they can see the action happening in the problem. During sharing time, Ms. McCann encourages all of her students to participate in the solution sharing and demonstrates some of the more complex strategies for the class.*

Questions for Discussion

1. How did Ms. McCann make the *How Many of Each?* problems more accessible for Courtney and Jasmine? Have you had students in your classroom who have struggled with these problems? How did you help your learners?

2. What are the important mathematical ideas that came up during sharing?

3. How does Ms. McCann help her range of learners both participate and learn from each other during the class discussion? What strategies do you use to do this in your classroom?

Challenging Highly Competent Learners

All teachers are faced with the task of meeting the needs of a diverse group of students. In this case, Gretchen Harris, a Grades 1–2 teacher, shares her strategies for creating meaningful activities to challenge some students in her classroom who are very competent in mathematics.

Each year brings with it a student who has an especially strong number sense. This year I have two students, Garrett and Fiona, who often require a "challenge."

Challenges are not meant to make certain students stand out as more special than other students; rather, they are viewed as the next step in the learning process. Therefore, challenges are offered when whatever work we have that day is finished and done well.

Challenges usually extend from an activity or a game that the rest of the class is working on that day. For example, when we were working on people and pet riddles, I wrote a few riddles with more elements for those students who finished early and were ready for more complexity.

Everyday classroom routines can also serve as a challenge for students. Fiona and Garrett often work on *Today's Number* (a Grade 2 routine) with varying constraints. For example, we were doing *Today's Number* the other day, and Fiona and Garrett both came up with a multiplication expression that equaled 100. So I challenged them to think of other ways to make 100 using only multiplication. They quickly came up with 100×1, 50×2, 25×4, 10×10, and 5×20. They soon requested that they be allowed to use a combination of multiplication and addition. They came up with $(2 \times 40) + 20 = 100$. The latter activity led to both Garrett and Fiona trying to figure out how division works, which they continue to attempt daily, usually by transforming a multiplication fact they know. Thinking about division has been their latest challenge if they finish early.

I have also modified many of the games we play to make them more challenging. For example, when we were playing *Make 50 Cents,* Garrett and Fiona started with 50 cents

each and subtracted down to 0. Then they played *Make a Dollar* and once they reached a dollar, they subtracted back to zero. They were forced to make trades immediately and required each other's assistance on occasion to make sure they were accurate.

I have found that the game *Roll and Record* is very easy to tailor to students' individual needs. To do so, I often have groups of students working with different numbers of number cubes. Some students play with two number cubes, others play with three number cubes, and a few students work their way up to using four. This type of modification works well as long as at least two students are in a similar spot mathematically. Having only one student operating at a level much higher than the rest of the class is much trickier because the games and activities requiring two people do not work, and you run the risk of isolating one student or creating a situation that may feel unfair to others.

The few times when I have had only one student who required a challenge, I relied heavily on generalizations. In my class we call the times when we try to prove something mathematical "Math Court." The students are the lawyers who present evidence to support their cases to me, the judge. I have found that students who are competent math thinkers often struggle to get their words out when it comes to proving something. For example, they may find it difficult to articulate why order does not matter when adding together a string of numbers. Although these types of generalizations are often difficult to explain, the students enjoy gathering evidence and presenting it to the class. They usually end up working with other students who are interested in the same topic. I once had a group of students working hard to try to put the pattern blocks in order from biggest to smallest, and as part of that activity to determine which pattern block was bigger: the blue rhombus or the square. Those are the best kind of adaptations—the ones that just emerge out of a need or interest of the students. However, when these spontaneous adaptations happen, I am sure to put the notion in my teacher toolbox for a time when someone else in another year's class is looking for a challenge.

I have thought a lot about meeting the needs of a diverse group of students. Accommodating highly competent learners is often especially difficult for teachers. I used to think it was about making the numbers harder (e.g., bigger), but that happens very rarely now. If a student is skilled with number work, adding bigger numbers really isn't that much of a challenge for them. In a school where teachers try to work "smarter not harder," the adaptations that are most useful end up looking more like next steps in learning than preferential treatment to a "gifted" few.

In this case, Ms. Harris shares how she meets the needs of a few highly competent learners in her classroom. Because she is prepared with activities that are natural extensions of the learning process, Ms. Harris is able to thoughtfully challenge the students who are ready without isolating the other students in the classroom. In this way, Ms. Harris is able to maintain a classroom community where the needs of all learners are valued and respected.

Questions for Discussion

1. In this case, Ms. Harris writes that when creating challenges for highly competent learners, just making the numbers bigger isn't really a challenge for most students. How does Ms. Harris go about making challenges for her students? What are some of the things that she considers about her students when creating challenges? What does she hope her students will learn by working on some of the challenges she mentions in this case?

2. Ms. Harris is careful to create an environment in which her students who get a challenge are not viewed as receiving preferential treatment. How does she go about creating this type of environment in her classroom?

3. How do you go about providing challenges for the students who are ready for more in your classroom?

Crayon Puzzles

In this case, first-grade teacher Carly Fredericks reflects on the experience two of her students had while working on Crayon Puzzles. *In doing so, she illustrates the complexities of trying to meet the needs of a broad range of learners.*

During math time today, I was struck by the range in confidence and competence in my class. The students were working individually or in pairs on *Crayon Puzzles.* After reflecting on the session, I realized that I had never been so intrigued and simultaneously perplexed by these problems as I was today.

On the one hand, I had Kim who was working so fast I could hardly keep up with her. She had a system for making a chart for all the possible combinations for 10. I watched as she made a T-chart and labeled the left side red and the right side blue. Next she wrote all the numbers from 10 to 0 going down the red column, then she wrote all the numbers from 0 to 10 going down the blue column. In one final stroke of the pencil, she circled four of the newly formed combinations.

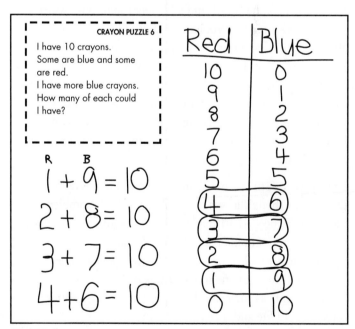

Kim's Work

She was like an artist at work, and before she added her name to the top of the paper, she wrote four equations to the left. It was clear that Kim knew how to solve this problem and had such facility with number facts that equal 10 that she barely looked up from the paper. It seemed like only seconds went by before she put her finished work in the basket and was off making a new choice.

I asked Kim to talk to me about her work. "Oh, it's easy. I make my chart for the number, then I write number sentences. I know I need to write R and B. You have to add those for red and blue or you wouldn't know what they are. See, you have to have more blue than red because that's what the problem says." It all seemed so effortless.

Devon was also working on *Crayon Puzzles.* Devon had shown that he had a strategy for solving *How Many of Each?* problems. He worked with counters. He knew how many counters he needed to start and then was able to break them into two subsets. He usually got three or four different solutions on his own but was not yet able to stick with the task long enough to find all the ways. If I asked him to revisit the task, he could find additional solutions. When he started working with problems that asked him to think about an additional condition (e.g., I have more blue crayons.), Devon was stuck. He seemed to consistently ignore that sentence in the problem. Although we had focused our class conversations on paying attention to this new part of the problem, I knew that learning in the larger group is not Devon's preferred way of working. I knew I needed to spend some focused time with him.

I asked Devon to tell me about his work. He treated the problem as though it was a *How Many of Each?* problem. He knew he needed 10 crayons and that some were blue and some were red. On his paper he had 5 and 5, 6 and 4, 9 and 1, and 4 and 6. In each pair he had written one number in blue and one in red. I was pleased to see the "turn around" as my class this year is known to call for 6 red and 4 blue and 4 red and 6 blue.

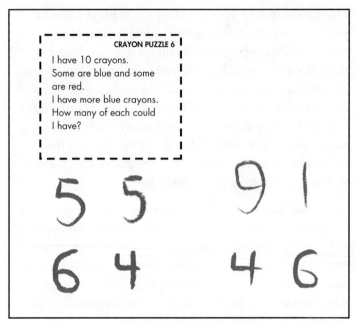

Devon's Work

Next I asked Devon to read the problem to me, and he read it aloud. "See, you have 10 crayons. You know, like 5 and 5. I guess they like red and blue because those are the colors they use. You need to find out how many red and blue." Devon never referred to the sentence about "I have more blue crayons."

Teacher: So this problem is about 10 crayons. Some are blue and some are red. I can see from your work that you found four ways to solve this problem.

Devon: Yup!

Teacher: I am wondering what this part means? [I pointed to the part of the problem about the more blues.]

Devon read the sentence aloud. I waited to see if he responded in any way. He did not.

Teacher: What do you think that means?

Devon: I guess I will have blue, and my sister will have red.

Teacher: Why would your sister have red?

Devon: Because I would have more.

Teacher: Did you think about this part when you were working on the problem before?

Devon: Kind of. I know I want more, so I think the answer is 9 and 1.

Devon made a motion with his hand to pick up his pencil. He began to cross off other answers. It did not seem to bother him that on his paper he had written 9 in red and 1 in blue.

Teacher: Before you write, please tell me more about what you are thinking.

Devon: I guess I don't need these (circling his pencil over the other answers).

Teacher: Why not?

Devon: I have to have the most and that is 9.

My conversation with Devon went on for a few more minutes, as I tried to help him consider other possible solutions. He didn't budge. He had decided that 9 was the most and that was the end. In time, I asked him to put his work away and to make another choice. He was happy to be "free" (as he said on leaving my side) from my questioning, but I knew I was not free from thinking about what next steps to take.

The balancing act in a classroom is monumental. In many ways this problem was too easy for Kim. At the same time it was, at this moment, too hard for Devon. As I looked around the classroom, I realized that all of the other students were able to make sense of this problem, though maybe not as effortlessly as Kim. As I considered how to help Devon move forward, I thought of the following questions:

- Would changing the number help for Devon?

- Should he go back and work on more *How Many of Each?* problems that did not have the additional constraint?

- Should I help him focus on what it means to have more?

- Does he see that he can have more than one solution?

The questions come easily, but the answers seem more out of reach. I've learned to use my questions to guide my next steps in hopes of finding an answer and helping a student make gains. It feels like trial and error, but I know that it is more than guessing. Though I don't always feel secure with my decision making, I know I start by looking at what each student can do to help make sense of what he/she is not able to do yet.

I also needed to consider Kim's needs. Like Devon, she was alone at her end of the range of learners, the only student who was working at this level of confidence and competence. My thoughts included changing the number for her, changing the constraint, and possibly adding a second constraint. It might be easy to dismiss her as she was so content with her efforts, but I want to make sure that her needs are met too.

Taking time to get to know each student is crucial in making sense of what each student can do and figuring out the next steps on their individual path to understanding. What matters most for me is putting each student's learning trajectory at the center of my attention. This allows me to make the best decisions I can to meet each student's needs as we work with the curriculum, modifying it if necessary, and strive for understanding, flexibility, and confidence in mathematics.

In this case, Carly Fredericks illustrates the challenges teachers face when trying to meet the needs of all learners. Although at the end of the reflection Ms. Fredericks has more questions than answers, it is clear that her questions will guide her as she thinks of the next steps for each of her learners.

Questions for Discussion

1. What are the important mathematical ideas that students are working on as they try to solve *Crayon Puzzles*? What does Kim understand about the math? What does Devon understand?

2. Ms. Frederick raises questions about what her next steps should be for both Devon and Kim. What are your thoughts about the questions she raises and the experiences she should provide for Devon and Kim?

3. Reflect on a time in your own classroom when you saw a similar range as students worked on a particular activity. What did you do to address the needs of the learners who completed the activity easily and those who had difficulty entering the problem? Were you satisfied with the accommodations that you made?

Language and Representation

How Many of Each?
Probing Student Understanding

In this case, Laura McCann, a first-grade teacher, works with Isabel to help her connect visual and numeric representations as she decomposes numbers in How Many of Each? *problems. Ms. McCann reflects on her own confusion about what Isabel does and does not understand.*

One of my struggling learners, Isabel, had finally grasped a foolproof way to approach *How Many of Each?* problems—using pictures. She would draw circles and sticks to show how many of each item she could have using a "staircase" representation. For example, if the total were 10, her paper would look like the following:

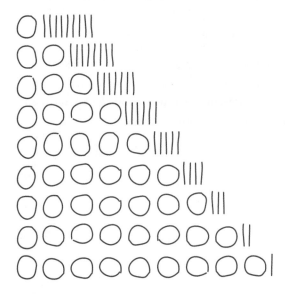

Isabel was very satisfied that she could use her method to easily find all the solutions. She did not attempt to use this visual information to write equations to show her solutions. This was something that I wanted to work on with her.

At this point, I tried to have her use the visual model she had created to help move her toward using equations to express the number relationships. She interpreted this at first as a request to find other ways to represent the number 9. She proceeded to show 9 as 9 squares, 9 tally marks, 9 fingers drawn on the page, and an equation: $1 + 1 + 1 + 1 + 1 + 1 + 1 + 1 + 1 = 9$.

I decided to sit down with her to demonstrate what I meant by using equations. I started by asking her to count the total number of circles in each row of nine and add that to the total number of sticks she had used in each row. Slowly, Isabel began to see what I was after and was able to write some of the equations to represent her work, like $1 + 8 = 9$, $2 + 7 = 9$, $3 + 6 = 9$, and so forth.

The students worked on a different, related problem the next day. I asked the class to come up with combinations of numbers to make a total of 10. As usual, Isabel began with her visual model of circles and sticks, representing all the possible ways for two quantities to be put together to make a total of 10. Again, I pressed her to use numeric representations for what she had drawn. The results were very interesting. Instead of writing equations to represent her "staircase" approach, she came up with different equations altogether. She began with a string of 1s added to make 10. Underneath this was a string of 2s added together to make 10, underneath was a string of 3s (and a 1) to make 10, a string of 4s (and a 2) to make 10, and a string of 5s to make 10. Her paper looked like this:

$1 + 1 + 1 + 1 + 1 + 1 + 1 + 1 + 1 + 1 = 10$

$2 + 2 + 2 + 2 + 2 = 10$

$3 + 3 + 3 + 1 = 10$

$4 + 4 + 2 = 10$

$5 + 5 = 10$

I was pleased that she was writing equations, but I wondered if this was another of her attempts to have a fail-safe system to approach the kinds of problems I was asking her to solve: just keep using the same number until you no longer can. Her equations did demonstrate some number sense, though I was unsure exactly what she understood about these combinations.

A few days later, we were working on 12. Predictably, Isabel began with her visual model of circles and sticks before she moved on to other possible solutions. She did write an equation to accompany most of her visual representations, and she did reuse her idea of repeated addition from the previous assignment. The only new attempt I noticed in her work was a turnaround she was trying out. She had written $5 + 5 + 2 = 12$ and then further on I saw $5 + 2 + 5 = 12$. I wondered if she had done it intentionally, or if it had just happened in an unrelated effort to find another possible way to make 12. In interviewing her, she was unable to articulate whether the two equations were related ideas, which brought me back to wondering about her number sense.

Thinking about Isabel's work over the last few days, I remain puzzled by several issues.

- Is she thinking about mathematical relationships as she solves problems or relying on a "recipe" that has worked for her in the past?

- Does she see the connection between her representations and the equations she writes?

- Does she understand that a number can be composed or decomposed in different ways?

I will use these questions to guide my work with her as we continue on our mathematical journey together.

In this case, Ms. McCann works with Isabel to help her make sense of a strategy she was using. Although Ms. McCann is pleased that Isabel has found a way to solve How Many of Each? *problems, she wants to push her toward using numeric representations rather than just visual representations. Although at the end of the session Ms. McCann still remains somewhat puzzled about the extent of Isabel's knowledge about numbers, she is able to formulate a series of questions to guide their work together.*

Questions for Discussion

1. Throughout this case, Ms. McCann feels puzzled about the extent of Isabel's number sense. What number knowledge do the problems require? What do you think Isabel's strategies demonstrate about her understanding of numbers? What do you think Ms. McCann's next steps should be to help Isabel build on her number foundation?

2. Have you had a student like Isabel in your classroom? What have you done to help such students write equations to represent math work and to expand their knowledge of number composition?

Who Is Talking?
Reflections on a Discussion

Discussions are a critical component in any mathematical curriculum. By listening to the ideas being shared by their students, teachers can gain significant insight into their students' mathematical thinking. In this case, Laura McCann, a first-grade teacher, realizes that it is also important to pay attention to which students are willing to share their thoughts during a discussion and which students are not.

In a discussion of strategies for solving the problem $9 - 3$ in a subtraction game, one of my students posed the problem $3 - 9$. Some of the students were familiar with the term *negative number,* but they had a limited understanding of what that meant. As the discussion evolved, I probed students to think about what "less than 0" could mean by contextualizing negative numbers.

Teacher: Today we are going to play a subtraction game that you have played already with number cubes. So if I roll a 9 and 3, what would I do?

Adriana: Take the 9 and then take away the 3.

Teacher: What would that be? Counting?

Henry: Down.

Teacher: So should the ending number be larger or smaller than the number you start with?

Class: Smaller.

Vanessa: If you started with the smaller number and subtract the bigger number, it would always be 0.

Henry: No, it would be in the negatives.

Teacher: What do you know about negative numbers?

Nico: They are lower than 0. If you go backward on the not negatives, you go to the negatives.

Teacher: Where do these numbers show up in real life? When we say "negative numbers," what do we mean? How can a number be less than 0?

I followed these questions by asking them to cup their hands in front of them. "Look into your hands, you hold nothing. How can you have less than that?" A silence followed; my students were really thinking now. I wondered how they would reconcile the difference between what they understood the definition to be and what the reality was looking like. Some of them could say that negative numbers are less than 0, but they had no way to see how that occurred in everyday life.

Maurice: You would have negatives.

Edward: It's only math; you can't do it in real life.

Edward's statement hit the nail on the head as to what my students seemed to understand about negative numbers. The students with any knowledge or experience were imagining the number line. They knew that once you got to 0, you kept going, only now you were in negative numbers.

Teacher: Negative numbers do happen in real life. Does anyone know where?

There was another pause, and I was inwardly debating whether to push this discussion or back off when a little voice called out, "In a building."

Maurice: Like in a building. If you see one side and then you see the other.

I was unsure what Maurice meant by the second half of his comment, but his remark sparked a new idea from Rob.

Rob: It could be from like the top floor to the basement and if there was another basement, it would be -1 of the basement.

Teacher: Let me draw something for you. [I drew a building on the easel chart, showing the ground, several floors up and several floors underground.] These floors are above the street, and then we also have these floors that go underground or under the street. This floor would be one below so it would be negative 1.

My students were counting down with me into negative numbers. As I was hearing them say, "One below (the ground), two below (the ground)," I was struck with another connection for negative numbers.

Teacher: When do people use the term *something below*?

Maurice: Like when it is 9 below 0.

Teacher: When would you hear that?

Beth: When it is really cold out.

The temperature discussion continued. I drew a thermometer for them to see again how the negative numbers dipped below 0. As my students were conversing about how cold it could be, Jonathan brought up the idea of value in negative numbers.

Jonathan: Negative 1 is more than negative 3.

Teacher: What does that mean in floors?

Leon: Closer to the street.

Henry: But 3 is more than 1; it doesn't make sense.

Rob: Yeah, but these are the negatives.

Edward: It's like a mirror.

Henry: You mean like a fun mirror?

Teacher: No, the numbers describe a distance from 0. Pretend I am having a party. I have 3 hats, but 9 people are coming to the party. I would be down 6 hats. Or if I was going out to lunch with Mrs. Adams and the total was $9 and Mrs. Adams only had $3, she would owe $6.

I could see that this discussion had given them all something new to think about when it came to negative numbers. For some students, it was mainly that there were negative numbers. The concept and language had been new to them. For others, it was a context for thinking about negative numbers; for others, it was the idea that the values of negative numbers seemed inverted or "fun house mirrored" from positive numbers.

As I wrapped up the discussion on the day's work, I reflected on who the participants had been. It was Vanessa who had made the initial comment about taking larger numbers from smaller ones. However, after that, the discussion participants were primarily boys. Beth was the only other girl who had braved a contribution. I started to wonder about that. The boys clearly seemed either to have more ideas about negative numbers or were more willing to risk a question or comment about them in a whole class discussion. There had been many misconceptions brought up by the boys, yet they continued to throw new ideas on the table. The girls had remained interested but silent, with the exception of the whole class counting down the floors of the building. I also considered the makeup of my group. There are 13 boys and 9 girls. Did the girls feel outnumbered? Would a different ratio have made the girls feel "safer" than the boys in a whole class discussion? Or was it simply the topic? When sharing problem-solving solutions with the group, I have an equal number of girls and boys who make a contribution. Was this because it feels safer to share something with the class when they are reasonably sure of the answer? These are questions I will continue to keep in my head as I observe future math conversations with this class.

Teachers must consider many factors when facilitating whole-class discussions. In this case, a remark casually made by a student launches Ms. McCann's first-grade class into an unexpected discussion about negative numbers. During the discussion, Ms. McCann is focused on helping her students develop a deeper understanding of negative numbers. When Ms. McCann later reflects on the discussion, she realizes that the primary participants were boys. She is left wondering why more boys participated than girls. The reflection that Ms. McCann engaged in, as well as the follow-up questions she generated, will certainly guide her work as she observes future classroom discussions.

Questions for Discussion

1. In this case, Ms. McCann notices that more boys than girls participated in the discussion about negative numbers. Ms. McCann wonders if the girls in her class are less willing to take mathematical risks. How might she have included more girls in this discussion? What could she do to follow up on this discussion, which might allow more girls to participate?

2. When you reflect on discussions in your classroom, what do you notice about who participates in terms of gender?

Seeing Connections: A First Grader Compares Representations of Number Sequences

This case begins while students in Gretchen Harris's first-grade classroom are discussing the connections they see between two activities, the Penny Jar *and* Staircase Towers, *from the unit* Color, Shape, and Number Patterns. *Both of these activities generate number sequences with a constant increase by establishing an initial amount—the "start with" number—and then adding a given quantity repeatedly. The specific problems that students were comparing both involved initial amounts of 1 with a constant change of 3. Ms. Harris's goal and expectation for this discussion was for her students to recognize this connection. However, one student was able to take her observations to an unexpected place.*

For some students, there was no discernible connection between the *Penny Jar* and *Staircase Towers* activities. They did not seem to notice that the numbers were the same until a peer pointed it out during the discussion. Others had the most nascent connections. "They both start at one," was as far as Danny could go.

But some students could see sophisticated similarities between *Staircase Towers* and the *Penny Jar.* Out of the blue, Joanna said, "The staircase tower is really a graph of the penny jar." I asked her to say more. She explained that each square on the tower was a penny. Each column showed how many you have in the penny jar on one day. Nate added on to what Joanna said by pointing out that the numbers underneath the columns in the tower matched the number of pennies in the jar, starting with the second column (4 cubes matched the 4 pennies of Day 1). The first column showed one cube, the "start with" number in the tower, which matched the "start with" penny in the jar for our penny jar pattern.

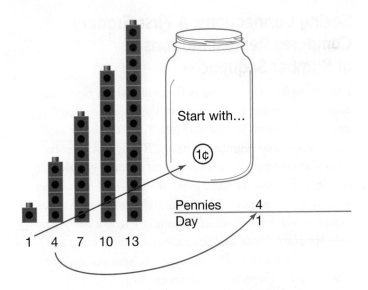

Pennies 4
Day 1

1 4 7 10 13

Looking at these graphs every day, Joanna has developed a clear schema of a bar graph. And while I never stopped to think that *Staircase Towers* could be a bar graph for *Penny Jar* sequences, Joanna recognized it immediately. To see how far her understanding went, I showed her some of her work with *Penny Jar* problems and asked her if she could tell me what the *Staircase Towers* graph would look like for a few of them. She had no problem pointing to the number of pennies in the jar at the beginning and describing that number as the "start with" number for the *Staircase Towers*. She then knew that what you added to the jar each day was the "step up" number on the graph. I found this very interesting because one of the places my students struggled with in *Staircase Towers* was how much to step up. The concept of adding more pennies to a jar each day seemed far easier for them to imagine or to represent with a drawing.

Joanna's ability to see the penny jar pattern as a staircase tower was also interesting because of the difference in the representations of each. The penny jar has its first number inside the jar, and the pattern continues numerically as a sequence written across the page.

I was intrigued that Joanna saw the staircase tower as a graphic representation. I wanted to understand her thinking about this and give her an opportunity to expand on it, so I approached her a little later in the day to interview her further. When I asked her how she figured out that the tower was a graph of the penny jar, she said she could just "see it." She referred to our graphing board in the class.

When students arrive each day, they sign in on the graphing board in response to a question a class member has written. Each student has a cube with his or her name and places it to indicate his or her response. Sometimes the question is as basic as "Did you brush your teeth this morning?" with "yes" and "no" as the choices. Other questions are more complex, such as "Which card picture did you think was the hardest to build?" with the card numbers from 1 to 10 listed across the bottom of the graph, and students placing their cubes above the card number. Most days begin with the class looking at the resulting bar graph and interpreting it in some way. With the card picture question, it became clear that one particular card was considered harder than any other.

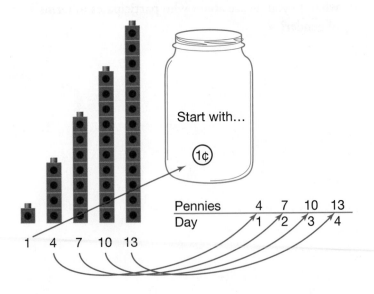

Pennies 4 7 10 13
Day 1 2 3 4

1 4 7 10 13

The number inside the jar has to be the first piece of the graph in *Staircase Towers*. I would have expected that Joanna's first graphing move would have been to take the first number in the sequence written linearly across the page and use that as the first tower in her graph, yet she knew it needed to be the number of pennies inside the jar before any are added. The questions that I'm left with are these: "Are there more links I could be making for other class members to help them see this connection? How important is having this understanding in first grade?"

In comparing these Penny Jar *and* Staircase Towers *problems, students in this classroom are working with the important idea that the same mathematical structure can underlie different situations. For most first graders, this understanding begins with recognizing that both of these problems produce the same sequence of numbers and develops as they try to explain why that is true (e.g., they both start with 1 and add 3 each time). Joanna is able to see this connection as she identifies the* Staircase Towers *as a graphic representation of the* Penny Jar *problem. Instead of pursuing this idea with the whole class, Ms. Harris decides to take the time to work individually with Joanna.*

Questions for Discussion

1. What are the mathematical ideas the students are working on in these activities? What is the goal of this particular discussion? In what way does Joanna's observation go beyond this goal?

2. Ms. Harris wonders if Joanna's understanding presents an opportunity to help other students make important connections about the underlying mathematics in both situations. What is your thinking about this question? How might Ms. Harris bring Joanna's idea to the rest of the class?

3. Think of a time in your classroom when a student raised an idea that was beyond the level of understanding of most of the class. Did you pursue this idea with the student who raised it? If so, how? Did you bring this idea to the rest of the class? If so, how?

How Many More? Understanding Through Sharing and Discussion

Ms. Lopez, a math resource teacher, has found that comparison problems are challenging for her group of first graders. In this case, she shares how providing her students with a familiar context to solve problems and a chance to share their strategies helped them make sense of the problem, clarify their thinking, and become more comfortable and confident with the mathematics.

Sharing is a time when students can learn from each other. I have made this part of the lesson an important moment, especially in working with students who struggle in math. Listening to each other and trying to understand each other's ideas promotes understanding.

I am presently working with a group of five first graders who struggle with math. Comparison problems are a challenge for these students. When presented with a question like "How many more does x have than y?" they will often add x and y to find how many in all. I have found, however, that when my students try to make sense of the question, they will often clarify it with new questions like the following: "Do you mean how many to catch up? Or how many to have the same?" Posed in this way, the questions involve a clear action and make the problem more accessible to them.

At the beginning of one of our sessions, we played the game *Make Ten*. When we finished the game, the students counted how many cards they had taken in the game. I used that information to create story problems.

The first problem said:

Adrian has 8 cards.

Michael has 12 cards.

Adrian wants to have the same number of cards as Michael.

How many more cards does Adrian need?

I read the story a couple of times, asked my students to visualize what I was saying, and then had them to say the story in their own words. They seemed to understand that Michael needed more cards to have the same amount as Adrian, and they needed to find out how many more cards he needed. My students worked by themselves and then shared their work. I asked Melissa to share first. She refused because she said she "messed up." She has had difficulties organizing her ideas and work. I understood how she felt and proposed that she listen to the other students' explanations to see if they made sense to her. She agreed.

I asked Michael to share his work. I chose him because he had trouble keeping track of the count. I noticed that at first Michael set out Adrian's 8 cards on one side of the table and his 12 cards on the other side. He went back to Adrian's cards and counted on until he got to 11. He realized he had counted wrong so he went back, counted up to 12 but had forgotten how many he had counted on. He counted again several times but had difficulties keeping track of the count. I suggested he use counters for each number he said. He did and added 4 orange cubes to the cards to show Adrian would need 4 more cards to have the same as Michael.

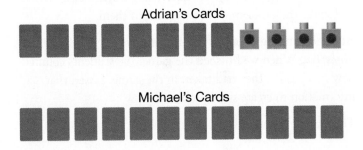

Adrian's Cards

Michael's Cards

I thought that explaining what he had done would help him solidify his thinking. In addition, I hoped that hearing Michael's strategy would help Melissa better understand how to solve the problem. When he shared his strategy, he focused on using the counters to keep track of the numbers.

I asked Melissa if she understood what Michael said. She was confused, so I rephrased it. As soon as I was done, Melissa exclaimed with excitement, "Oh! Now I get it!" And went

back to her work to fix it. As I mentioned earlier, Melissa was confused and had difficulties organizing her ideas. Her initial work showed 8 circles to represent Adrian's cards and 12 circles to represent Michael's cards, but she didn't know what to do with them. After listening to Michael's explanation and my rephrasing, she turned the page around, drew a group of 8 circles, labeled it 8, drew a group of 4 circles, and labeled it 4. She wrote 12 on top of both groups. She went ahead to explain her work: "This is what Adrian has. So he needs 4 more cards to have 12." She then wrote $8 + 4 = 12$.

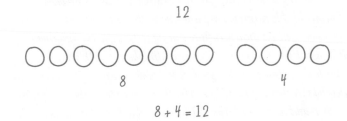

Listening to her peers helped Melissa clarify her confusion. Although she couldn't follow Michael very clearly at first, when I rephrased his ideas, I kept referring back to his words and work. I was explaining it not from my own understanding but from another student's understanding. This became very accessible to Melissa. I didn't have to ask her to share; she just went ahead and explained her thinking to us. This was a very important moment in her learning. She was excited about being able to figure it out and overcome her initial insecurities. I have noticed that when students explain their ideas to each other, they understand them more easily than if I try to explain them. They are also more engaged in the conversation.

A few days later, I presented a missing addend problem to my students:

I had 14 cards on the table. I shuffled the deck of cards; some fell on the floor, and now I have only 8 on the table. How many cards fell on the floor?

After listening to the problem, Melissa said: "Uh! Remember? This is just like the other problem. We need to know how many cards to get from 8 to 14."

I was pleased to see Melissa making connections between the two situations. She now had experiences she could think about to help build new understandings. The opportunity to talk ideas through and share her work helped her understand what had been difficult to her.

In this case, Ms. Lopez illustrates how providing a familiar context and fostering the sharing of ideas can be powerful for students. Through Ms. Lopez's careful questioning, Michael had an opportunity to clarify his thinking, while Melissa was introduced to a strategy that helped her make sense of the problem. Both students left the session with a more solid understanding of comparison situations and renewed confidence in their mathematical abilities.

Questions for Discussion

1. What are the important mathematical ideas that students are working on as they try to solve comparison problems? How did Ms. Lopez make use of context to build her students' understanding of comparison problems?

2. What does Michael understand about the math? What does Melissa understand? What role did Ms. Lopez play in the sharing session that helped the students make sense of the mathematics? How did the sharing session help both of these students move forward with their mathematical thinking? How did Melissa apply this understanding to her work with the missing addend problem? What role did representations play in Michael's work and Melissa's work?

3. What experiences would you provide for Michael and Melissa or for students like them to help them build on these sessions?

The strands are divided into Math Emphases.

The Math Emphases may be covered in one or more units. The Math Emphases are further subdivided into Math Focus Points.

Each strand is labeled with a grade level.

The content is organized around five strands.

GRADE 1

Number and Operations

Counting and Quantity Developing strategies for accurately counting a set of objects by ones

Unit 1 Math Focus Points
- Counting a set of up to 20 objects by 1s
- Practicing the rote counting sequence forward and backward, from 1 to 30
- Connecting number names and written numbers to the quantities they represent
- Developing and analyzing visual images for quantities up to 10

Unit 2 Math Focus Points
- Counting a set of objects

Unit 3 Math Focus Points
- Practicing the rote counting sequence forward and backward, starting from any number 1–60
- Developing and analyzing visual images for quantities
- Accurately counting a set of objects by ones, up to 60
- Practicing the oral counting sequence from 1 to 100
- Writing the sequence of numbers (as high as students know)
- Identifying and using patterns in the sequence of numbers to 100

KINDERGARTEN

Number and Operations

Counting and Quantity Developing strategies for accurately counting a set of objects by ones

Unit 1 Math Focus Points

◆ Counting the number of students in the class

◆ Using the calendar to count days

◆ Connecting number names, numerals, and quantities

◆ Establishing one-to-one correspondence between equal groups (e.g. students and cubes)

◆ Developing strategies for accurately counting and keeping track of quantities up to the number of students in the class

◆ Creating an equivalent set

◆ Counting, creating, and representing quantities

Unit 2 Math Focus Points

◆ Developing strategies for accurately counting and keeping track of quantities up to 12

◆ Connecting number words, numerals, and quantities

◆ Developing visual images for quantities up to 6

◆ Counting backwards

Unit 3 Math Focus Points

◆ Counting, creating, and representing quantities

◆ Counting 12 objects

Unit 4 Math Focus Points

◆ Counting a set of objects and creating an equivalent set

◆ Connecting number words, numerals, and quantities

◆ Keeping track of a growing set of objects

◆ Counting spaces and moving on a gameboard

◆ Creating a set of a given size

◆ Developing and analyzing visual images for quantities up to 10

Unit 6 Math Focus Points

◆ Developing and analyzing visual images for quantities up to 10

◆ Counting spaces and moving on a game board

◆ Developing strategies for accurately counting and keeping track of quantities up to 20

◆ Using subsets to count a set of objects

Unit 7 Math Focus Points

◆ Counting and keeping track of quantities

◆ Matching sets with a 1-to-1 correspondence

◆ Working with 2-to-1 correspondence

◆ Counting by groups of 2

Counting and Quantity Developing an understanding of the magnitude and position of numbers

Unit 2 Math Focus Points

◆ Comparing two (or more) quantities to determine which is more

◆ Ordering quantities from least to most

◆ Developing language for comparing quantities (more, greater, less, fewer, most, least, fewest, same, and equal to)

Unit 4 Math Focus Points

◆ Developing an understanding of more than and fewer than

◆ Comparing two quantities to determine which is more

Unit 7 Math Focus Points

◆ Comparing two quantities to determine which is more

Counting and Quantity Developing the idea of equivalence

Unit 2 Math Focus Points

◆ Creating an equivalent set

◆ Considering whether order matters when you count

Unit 6 Math Focus Points

◆ Creating an equivalent set

◆ Counting and comparing quantities to 20 to determine which is more

Whole Number Operations Using manipulatives, drawings, tools, and notation to show strategies and solutions

Unit 1 Math Focus Points

◆ Exploring math manipulatives and their attributes

◆ Using the calendar as a tool for keeping track of time and events

◆ Representing quantities with pictures, numbers, objects, and/or words

Unit 2 Math Focus Points

◆ Representing quantities with pictures, numbers, objects, and/or words

◆ Using numerals to represent quantities

◆ Using a Ten-Frame to develop visual images of quantities up to 10

Unit 4 Math Focus Points

◆ Recording measurements with pictures, numbers, and/or words

◆ Using numbers to represent quantities and to record how many

◆ Using a Ten-Frame to develop visual images of quantities up to 10

◆ Recording an arrangement of a quantity

Unit 6 Math Focus Points

◆ Using numbers, and/or addition notation, to describe arrangements of objects, to record how many, and to represent an addition situation

◆ Using numbers, pictures, and/or words to represent a quantity or measurement, or a solution to a problem

Whole Number Operations Making sense of and developing strategies to solve addition and subtraction problems with small numbers

Unit 4 Math Focus Points

◆ Finding the total after a small amount (1, 2, 3) is added to a set of up to 7

◆ Combining two amounts

◆ Modeling the action of combining and separating situations

◆ Separating one amount from another

◆ Adding or subtracting one to/from numbers up to 10

◆ Adding to or subtracting from one quantity to make another quantity

◆ Decomposing numbers in different ways

◆ Exploring combinations of a number (e.g., 6 is 3 and 3 and also 5 and 1)

◆ Thinking strategically about moves on a gameboard

Unit 6 Math Focus Points

- Decomposing numbers in different ways
- Finding the total after 1, 2, or 3 is added to, or subtracted from, a set
- Combining single-digit numbers, with totals to 20
- Modeling the action of combining and separating situations
- Separating one amount from another
- Developing strategies for solving addition and subtraction story problems
- Finding combinations of a five and six
- Considering combinations of a number (e.g., 6 is 3 and 3 and also 5 and 1)
- Beginning to recognize that some problems have more than one solution
- Thinking strategically about moves on a gameboard

KINDERGARTEN

Patterns and Functions

Repeating Patterns Constructing, describing, and extending repeating patterns

Unit 3 Math Focus Points

- Copying, constructing, comparing, describing, and recording repeating patterns
- Determining what comes next in a repeating pattern
- Comparing repeating and non-repeating arrangements
- Distinguishing between patterns and non-patterns
- Constructing a variety of patterns using the same elements
- Comparing different kinds of patterns

Repeating Patterns Identifying the unit of a repeating pattern

Unit 3 Math Focus Points

- Identifying the unit of a repeating pattern
- Counting the number of units in a repeating pattern
- Extending a repeating pattern by adding on units to the pattern

KINDERGARTEN

Data Analysis

Data Analysis Sorting and classifying

Unit 1 Math Focus Points

- Identifying attributes (e.g. color, size, and shape) and developing language to describe them
- Comparing how objects are the same and different
- Finding objects that share one attribute
- Using attributes to sort a group of objects

Unit 3 Math Focus Points

- Finding objects that share one attribute
- Using attributes to sort a group of objects
- Comparing how objects are the same and different
- Observing and describing
- Using information to figure out what is missing

Unit 7 Math Focus Points

- Identifying the attributes of an object
- Identifying an attribute that is common to several objects
- Comparing how objects are the same and different
- Using attributes to sort a set of objects
- Grouping data into categories based on similar attributes
- Sorting a set of objects or data in different ways

Data Analysis Carrying out a data investigation

Unit 1 Math Focus Points

- Collecting and keeping track of survey data
- Describing and comparing the number of pieces of data in each category
- Interpreting results to a data investigation

Unit 7 Math Focus Points

- Choosing a survey question with two possible responses
- Collecting and keeping track of survey data
- Interpreting results of a data investigation
- Using data to solve a problem

Data Analysis Representing data

Unit 7 Math Focus Points

- Making a representation of a set of data
- Seeing the 1-to-1 correspondence between a set of data and a representation of this data

Geometry

Features of Shape Describing, identifying, comparing, and sorting two- and three-dimensional shapes

Unit 1 Math Focus Point

- Developing language to describe shapes, position, and quantity

Unit 5 Math Focus Points

- Developing language to describe and compare 2-D and 3-D shapes and their attributes
- Relating 2-D and 3-D shapes to real-world objects
- Describing the attributes of circles and rectangles
- Describing the attributes of triangles and squares
- Exploring relationships among pattern block shapes
- Comparing the faces of different 3-D shapes and the faces of a single 3-D shape
- Exploring materials
- Relating 3-D objects to 2-D pictures of 3-D shapes
- Matching a 3-D block to a 2-D outline of one of the block faces
- Exploring Geoblocks and their attributes

Features of Shape Composing and decomposing two- and three-dimensional shapes

Unit 5 Math Focus Points

- Constructing 2-D shapes
- Finding combinations of shapes that fill an area
- Constructing 3-D shapes
- Combining 3-D shapes to make a given 3-D shape

Measurement

Linear Measurement Understanding length

Unit 2 Math Focus Points

- Directly comparing two objects to determine which is longer
- Sorting objects into two categories, according to length
- Developing language to describe and compare lengths (long, longer than, short, shorter than, the same, equal to)

Linear Measurement Understanding length and using linear units

Unit 4 Math Focus Points

- Understanding what length is
- Identifying the longest dimension of an object
- Comparing lengths of different objects
- Repeating multiple nonstandard units to quantify length
- Developing strategies for measuring the length of an object

Unit 6 Math Focus Points

- Repeating multiple nonstandard units to quantify length

Classroom Routines

Today's Question

Units 2–7 Math Focus Points

- Collecting, counting, representing, describing, and comparing data

Patterns on the Pocket Chart

Units 3–7 Math Focus Points

- Determining what comes next in a repeating pattern
- Describing repeating patterns

Calendar

Units 1–7 Math Focus Points

- Using the calendar as a tool for keeping track of time
- Developing strategies for counting accurately

Attendance

Units 1–7 Math Focus Points

- Developing strategies for counting accurately
- Considering whether order matters when you count
- Comparing quantities
- Counting forward and backward

GRADE 1

Number and Operations

Counting and Quantity Developing an understanding of the magnitude and position of numbers

Unit 1 Math Focus Points

- Ordering a set of numbers and quantities up to 12
- Comparing two quantities up to 20 to see which is larger
- Developing an understanding of how the quantities in the counting sequence are related: each number is 1 more or 1 less than the number before or after it

Unit 6 Math Focus Points

- Reasoning about more, less, and equal amounts
- Finding a solution that fits several clues

Counting and Quantity Developing strategies for accurately counting a set of objects by ones

Unit 1 Math Focus Points

- Counting a set of up to 20 objects by 1s
- Practicing the rote counting sequence forward and backward, from 1 to 30
- Connecting number names and written numbers to the quantities they represent
- Developing and analyzing visual images for quantities up to 10

Unit 2 Math Focus Points

- Counting a set of objects

Unit 3 Math Focus Points

- Practicing the rote counting sequence forward and backward, starting from any number 1–60
- Developing and analyzing visual images for quantities
- Accurately counting a set of objects by ones, up to 60
- Practicing the oral counting sequence from 1 to 100
- Writing the sequence of numbers (as high as students know)
- Identifying and using patterns in the sequence of numbers to 100

Unit 6 Math Focus Points

- Developing strategies for counting and combining groups of dots

Unit 8 Math Focus Points

- Counting and keeping track of amounts up to 60
- Counting on from a known quantity
- Organizing objects to count them more efficiently
- Identifying and using patterns in the number sequence and on the 100 chart
- Identifying, reading, writing, and sequencing number to 100 and beyond
- Counting and combining things that come in groups of 1, 2, 4, 5, and 10
- Counting by 2s, 5s, and 10s
- Exploring a 2:1 (the number of hands in a group of people) and a 5:1 relationship (the number of fingers and hands in a group)
- Counting by numbers other than 1
- Developing strategies for organizing sets of objects so that they are easy to count and combine
- Developing meaning for counting by groups of ten
- Considering a 2-digit number as tens and ones

Number Composition Composing numbers up to 20 with 2 or more addends

Unit 1 Math Focus Points

◆ Finding and exploring relationships among combinations of numbers up to 10

◆ Recording combinations of two numbers that make a certain total

◆ Solving a problem with multiple solutions

◆ Solving a problem in which the total and one part are known

Unit 2 Math Focus Points

◆ Finding the sum of multiple addends

Unit 3 Math Focus Points

◆ Finding as many 2-addend combinations of a number as possible

◆ Finding and exploring relationships among combinations of numbers up to 15

◆ Solving a problem in which the total and one part are known

◆ Proving that all the possible combinations have been found

◆ Developing the strategy of counting on

Unit 6 Math Focus Points

◆ Developing fluency with the 2-addend combinations of 10

◆ Finding relationships among different combinations of numbers up to 20

◆ Using $5 + 5$ to reason about other combinations of 10

◆ Finding as many 2-addend combinations of a number as possible

◆ Trying to prove that all the possible 2-addend combinations of a number have been found

Unit 8 Math Focus Points

◆ Thinking about numbers to 20 in terms of how they relate to 10 (e.g., $10 +$ _____ or < 10)

Number Composition Representing numbers by using equivalent expressions

Unit 3 Math Focus Point

◆ Generating equivalent expressions for a number

Unit 6 Math Focus Points

◆ Generating equivalent expressions for a number

Unit 8 Math Focus Points

◆ Determining equivalent expressions for a given expression (e.g., $7 + 8 = 10 +$ _____)

Whole Number Operations Making sense of and developing strategies to solve addition and subtraction problems with small numbers

Unit 1 Math Focus Points

◆ Visualizing and retelling the action in an addition situation

◆ Modeling the action of an addition problem with counters or drawings

◆ Finding the total of two or more quantities up to a total of 20 by counting all, counting on, or using number combinations

◆ Seeing that adding the same two numbers (e.g., 4 and 3) results in the same total, regardless of context (e.g., number cubes, cards, objects)

Unit 3 Math Focus Points

◆ Visualizing and retelling the action in addition and subtraction situations involving removal

◆ Estimating whether an amount is more or less than a given quantity

◆ Finding the total of two or more quantities up to a total of 20 by counting all, counting on, or using number combinations

◆ Modeling the action of an addition or subtraction (removal) problem with counters or drawings

◆ Developing counting on as a strategy for combining two numbers

- Subtracting one number from another, with initial totals of up to 12
- Developing strategies for solving addition and subtraction (removal) problems
- Seeing that subtracting the same two numbers (e.g., 6 from 10) results in the same difference regardless of context (e.g., number and dot cubes, cards, objects)
- Solving story problems about comparing lengths

Unit 6 Math Focus Points

- Solving related story problems
- Solving a problem in which the total and one part are known
- Adding 2 or more single-digit numbers
- Visualizing, retelling, and modeling the action in addition and subtraction (removal) situations
- Subtracting one number from another, with initial totals of up to 12
- Developing strategies for solving addition and subtraction story problems
- Solving addition and subtraction story problems

Unit 8 Math Focus Points

- Adding single-digit numbers

Unit 9 Math Focus Point

- Counting and adding to compare the distances of different paths

Whole Number Operations Using manipulatives, drawings, tools, and notation to show strategies and solutions

Unit 1 Math Focus Points

- Using the number line as a tool for counting
- Introducing standard notation for comparing quantities (greater than, less than, and equal to)
- Introducing and using standard notation ($+$ and $=$) to represent addition situations
- Recording a solution to a problem
- Representing number combinations with numbers, pictures, and/or words

Unit 3 Math Focus Points

- Using the number line as a tool for counting
- Connecting written numbers and standard notation ($>, <, +, -, =$) to the quantities and actions they represent
- Using numbers and standard notation ($>, <, +, -, =$) to record
- Recording solutions to a problem
- Using the equal sign to show equivalent expressions
- Developing methods for recording addition and subtraction (removal) strategies
- Seeing the 100 chart as a representation of the counting numbers to 100

Unit 6 Math Focus Points

- Using numbers and standard notation ($+, -, =$) to record
- Developing strategies for recording solutions to story problems

Unit 8 Math Focus Points

- Using addition notation ($+, =$) to record
- Recording strategies for counting and combining
- Considering notation for equivalent expressions (e.g., $7 + 8 = 10 + 5$)

Computational Fluency Knowing addition combinations of 10

Unit 8 Math Focus Points

◆ Developing fluency with the 2-addend combinations of 10

◆ Solving a problem in which the total (10) and one part are known

GRADE 1

Patterns and Functions

Repeating Patterns Constructing, describing, and extending repeating patterns

Unit 2 Math Focus Points

◆ Using a repeated unit to create a pattern

◆ Seeing how changing the unit affects the whole pattern

Unit 7 Math Focus Points

◆ Identifying what comes next in a repeating pattern

◆ Using the word *pattern* to describe some kind of regularity in a sequence

Repeating Patterns Identifying the unit of a repeating pattern

Unit 7 Math Focus Points

◆ Representing a repeating unit in more than one way (for example, representing a red–blue–red–blue cube pattern with the movements clap–slap knees–clap–slap knees)

◆ Comparing repeating and non-repeating sequences

◆ Describing a repeating pattern as a sequence built from a part that repeats over and over called the *unit*

◆ Identifying the unit of a repeating pattern

◆ Extending a repeating pattern by adding on units to the pattern

◆ Identifying what comes several steps beyond the visible part of a repeating pattern

◆ Comparing repeating patterns that have the same structure (for example, ABC), but different elements (for example, red–blue–green and yellow–orange–black)

◆ Comparing repeating patterns that have the same length of unit, but different structures (for example, red–blue–green and red–red–blue both have 3-element units)

Number Sequences Constructing, describing, and extending number sequences with constant increments generated by various contexts

Unit 7 Math Focus Points

◆ Associating counting numbers with elements of a repeating pattern

◆ Determining the element of a repeating pattern associated with a particular counting number

◆ Determining and describing the number sequence associated with one of the elements in the unit of a repeating pattern (e.g., the numbers associated with B in an AB pattern are 2, 4, 6, 8...)

◆ Modeling a constant rate of increase with concrete materials

◆ Describing how a number sequence represents a situation with a constant rate of change

◆ Extending a number sequence associated with a situation with a constant rate of change

◆ Determining how and why the same number sequences can be generated by different contexts

GRADE 1

Data Analysis

Data Analysis Sorting and classifying

Unit 4 Math Focus Points

- Describing attributes of objects
- Using attributes to sort a set of objects
- Looking carefully at a group of objects to determine how they have been sorted

Data Analysis Representing data

Unit 4 Math Focus Points

- Making a representation to communicate the results of a survey
- Making sense of data representations, including pictures, bar graphs, tallies, and Venn diagrams
- Comparing what different representations communicate about a set of data
- Using equations to show how the sum of the responses in each category equals the total responses collected
- Organizing data in numerical order

Data Analysis Describing data

Unit 4 Math Focus Points

- Describing and comparing the number of pieces of data in each category or at each value and interpreting what the data tell you about the group
- Understanding that the sum of the pieces of data in all the categories equals the number of people surveyed
- Using data to compare how two groups are similar or different

Data Analysis Designing and carrying out a data investigation

Unit 4 Math Focus Points

- Interpreting results of a data investigation
- Choosing a survey question
- Making a plan for gathering data
- Collecting and keeping track of survey data

GRADE 1

Geometry

Features of Shape Describing, identifying, and comparing two-dimensional and three-dimensional shapes

Unit 1 Math Focus Points

- Exploring the characteristics of cubes, pattern blocks, Geoblocks, and Power Polygons

Unit 2 Math Focus Points

- Identifying common attributes of a group of shapes
- Describing, comparing, and naming 2-D shapes
- Developing visual images of and language for describing 2-D shapes
- Recognizing that there are many types of quadrilaterals (e.g., rectangles, trapezoids, squares, rhombuses)
- Identifying and making triangles and quadrilaterals of different shapes and sizes
- Identifying characteristics of triangles and quadrilaterals
- Noticing shapes in the environment

Unit 9 Math Focus Points

- Developing vocabulary to describe 3-D shapes and their attributes
- Comparing size, shape, and orientation of objects
- Identifying the characteristics of 3-D objects by touch
- Describing a rectangular prism
- Comparing rectangular prisms
- Observing and describing characteristics of 3-D shapes
- Recognizing shapes in the world
- Describing 3-D structures
- Relating the size and shape of an object to its use
- Planning a geometric structure with limited space and materials

Features of Shape Composing and decomposing two-dimensional shapes

Unit 2 Math Focus Points

- Covering a region without gaps or overlaps using multiple shapes
- Decomposing shapes in different ways
- Finding different combinations of shapes that fill the same area
- Seeing relationships between squares and triangles
- Altering designs to use more or fewer pieces to cover the same space
- Examining how shapes can be combined to make other shapes

Features of Shape Exploring the relationships between two-dimensional and three-dimensional shapes

Unit 9 Math Focus Points

- Matching a 3-D object to a 2-D outline of one of its faces
- Matching a 3-D object to a 2-D picture of the object
- Making 3-D objects out of 2-D pieces
- Making a 2-D representation of a 3-D object or structure
- Building a 3-D construction from a 2-D representation

- Visualizing and estimating the paces and turns required to follow a particular path
- Giving, following, and recording directions for following a path

GRADE 1

Measurement

Linear Measurement Understanding length

Unit 3 Math Focus Points

- Considering attributes that can be measured (e.g., length, perimeter, area)

Unit 5 Math Focus Points

- Understanding what length is and how it can be measured
- Measuring lengths using different-sized units
- Identifying the longest dimension of an object
- Comparing lengths to determine which is longer
- Identifying contexts in which measurement is used
- Understanding the meaning of at least in the context of linear measurement

Linear Measurement Using linear units

Unit 5 Math Focus Points

- Developing accurate measurement techniques
- Describing measurements that are in between whole numbers of units
- Understanding that measurements of the same length should be the same when they are measured twice or by different people using the same unit
- Understanding that measuring an object using different-lengths units will result in different measurements
- Measuring length by iterating a single unit

Linear Measurement Measuring with standard units

Unit 5 Math Focus Point

- Using inch tiles to measure objects in inches

GRADE 1

Classroom Routines

Start With/Get To

Units 1-8 Math Focus Points

- Connecting written numbers and number names
- Using the number line as a tool for counting
- Practicing the forward and backward counting sequences with numbers up to 100
- Using the 100 chart as a tool for counting
- Counting by 5s and 10s

Morning Meeting

Units 1-9 Math Focus Points

- Developing strategies for counting accurately (Attendance, Calendar, Weather)
- Using the calendar as a tool for keeping track of time (Calendar)
- Developing vocabulary to talk about time (morning, noon, midday, afternoon, etc.) and sequence (first, next, last, before, after, etc.) (The Daily Schedule, Calendar)
- Collecting and recording data (Weather)
- Estimating quantities up to about 30
- Adding small amounts to or subtracting small amounts from a familiar number
- Investigating numbers that can (and cannot) be made into groups of two
- Naming and telling time to the hour on digital and analog clocks
- Associating times on the hour with daily events

Quick Images

- Counting, describing, and comparing data
- Making sense of a variety of representations of data

Units 1-6 and 8-9 Math Focus Points

- Developing and analyzing visual images for quantities up to 10
- Recreating an arrangement of objects
- Finding the total of two or more single-digit quantities
- Developing visual images of, and language for describing, 2-D shapes
- Identifying names and attributes of 2-D shapes
- Finding the total of two or more equal groups
- Exploring relationships among combinations
- Identifying and naming coins
- Developing fluency with the addition combinations that make 10
- Using known combinations (i.e., combinations that make 10) to combine numbers
- Using standard notation ($+$, $-$, $=$) to write equations

Tell a Story

Units 7-9 Math Focus Points

- Connecting standard notation ($+$, $-$, $=$) to the actions and relationships they represent
- Creating a story problem for a given expression
- Developing strategies for adding and subtracting small numbers
- Solving related problems

Quick Surveys

Units 5-7 and 9 Math Focus Points

- Collecting, counting, representing, describing, and comparing data
- Interpreting different representations of data including: pictures, bar graphs, tallies, and Venn diagrams

GRADE 2

Number and Operations

Counting and Quantity Developing strategies for accurately counting a set of objects by ones and groups

Unit 1 Math Focus Points

- ◆ Counting sets of up to 60 objects
- ◆ Developing strategies for counting accurately
- ◆ Counting a quantity in more than one way
- ◆ Developing and analyzing visual images for quantities up to 10
- ◆ Counting by groups of 10

Unit 3 Math Focus Points

- ◆ Looking at patterns and developing fluency with skip counting by 2s, 5s, and 10s
- ◆ Considering the relationship between skip counting and grouping
- ◆ Counting by groups of 2, 5, and 10
- ◆ Noticing and describing a 2:1 relationship (e.g., there are 2 legs for every 1 person)
- ◆ Solving problems that involve equal groups
- ◆ Knowing that the size of a group remains constant no matter how it is counted (by 1s, 2s, 5s, or 10s)

Counting and Quantity Counting by equal groups

Unit 3 Math Focus Points

- ◆ Investigating numbers that can and cannot be made into groups of two or two equal groups
- ◆ Understanding that any number that can be divided into groups of two can also be divided into two equal groups (and vice versa)
- ◆ Characterizing even and odd numbers as those that do or do not make groups of two (partners) and two equal groups (teams)
- ◆ Considering whether observations about even or odd numbers apply to all even numbers or all odd numbers

Unit 5 Math Focus Points

- ◆ Counting by and adding equal groups, such as 2s and 5s

Unit 6 Math Focus Points

- ◆ Skip counting by 2s, 5s, and 10s
- ◆ Identifying patterns in the multiples of 2, 5, and 10
- ◆ Using the relationship between 5 and 10, and between nickels and dimes, to solve problems
- ◆ Thinking about the structure of 100 in terms of groups of 5 and 10

Unit 8 Math Focus Points

- ◆ Counting a set of objects by equal groups

Counting and Quantity Developing an understanding of the magnitude and sequence of numbers up to 100

Unit 1 Math Focus Points

- ◆ Using the number line to reason about, and keep track of information about, the magnitude and relationship of numbers
- ◆ Developing an understanding of the structure of the 100 chart
- ◆ Counting, writing, and reading numbers sequentially from 1 to 100 and beyond
- ◆ Identifying and using patterns in the structure of the number system

Unit 6 Math Focus Points

- ◆ Becoming familiar with the structure of the 100 chart
- ◆ Developing fluency with the sequence of numbers from 1 to 100
- ◆ Finding and using patterns in the sequence of numbers
- ◆ Using the 100 chart to reason about, and keep track of, information about the magnitude and relationship of numbers

Whole Number Operations Making sense of and developing strategies to solve addition and subtraction problems with totals up to 100

Unit 1 Math Focus Points

- Generating equivalent expressions for a number
- Comparing two amounts under 45 to find the difference
- Combining two quantities with totals up to 45
- Visualizing, retelling, and modeling the action of addition and subtraction (as removal) situations
- Using known combinations (e.g., combinations that make 10) to compose, decompose, and combine numbers
- Subtracting a quantity from a whole of up to 30
- Solving addition and subtraction (as removal) story problems
- Doubling a quantity

Unit 3 Math Focus Points

- Using known combinations to add two or more numbers
- Comparing a number to 20 to find the difference
- Visualizing, retelling, and modeling the action of a variety of addition and subtraction situations
- Developing strategies for solving a variety of addition and subtraction story problems with totals up to 45 and recording work
- Solving problems with an unknown change
- Combining coins to a total of 50¢
- Solving an addition story problem by counting on or breaking numbers apart

Unit 4 Math Focus Points

- Developing strategies for combining multiple addends

Unit 6 Math Focus Points

- Developing efficient methods for adding and subtracting 2-digit numbers
- Adding tens and ones to combine 2-digit numbers

- Adding 2-digit numbers by keeping one number whole
- Noticing what happens to the tens place when a multiple of 10 is added or subtracted
- Naming and comparing strategies for adding and subtracting two-digit numbers
- Determining the difference between a number and a multiple of 10 up to 100.
- Adding 2-digit numbers
- Adding multiples of 5 and 10, up to 100
- Adding coin amounts, up to $1.00
- Determining the difference between a given amount and $1.00
- Adding and subtracting 10 and multiples of 10 to/from any number
- Subtracting amounts from 100 or $1.00, down to 0

Unit 8 Math Focus Points

- Subtracting amounts from 100
- Visualizing, retelling, and modeling the action of addition and subtraction situations
- Developing efficient methods for adding, subtracting, and notating strategies
- Solving subtraction problems by subtracting in parts
- Solving subtraction problems by adding up or subtracting back to find the difference
- Comparing problems in which the amount subtracted differs by 1
- Adding 2-digit numbers by keeping one number whole
- Adding 2-digit numbers by adding tens and ones
- Noticing what happens to place value when two 2-digit numbers with a sum over 100 are combined
- Thinking about what happens if you subtract 1 more or 1 less

Unit 9 Math Focus Points

- Solving comparison problems by finding the difference between two measurements

Whole Number Operations Using manipulatives, drawings, tools, and notation to show strategies and solutions

Unit 1 Math Focus Points

◆ Establishing use of tools, routines, and expectations for math class

◆ Using standard notation ($>, <, +, -, =$) to describe arrangements of cubes, to record expressions that equal a given number, to compare quantities, to represent addition and subtraction situations, and to represent doubling

◆ Using the number line to reason about, and keep track of information about, the magnitude and relationship of numbers

◆ Recording strategies for solving problems, including addition and subtraction story problems

◆ Using equations to record

◆ Connecting standard notation for addition and subtraction ($+, -, =$) to the quantities and actions that the signs and symbols represent

◆ Using a rectangular array to model doubling

Unit 3 Math Focus Points

◆ Using the calculator as a mathematical tool

◆ Using standard notation ($+, -, =$) to represent a variety of addition and subtraction situations

◆ Telling stories to match given equations

◆ Using tally marks to represent groups of 5

Unit 6 Math Focus Points

◆ Writing an equation that represents a problem

◆ Developing efficient methods for notating addition and subtraction strategies

◆ Visualizing and making jumps of multiples of 5 on the 100 chart

◆ Using the 100 chart and the number line to model addition

◆ Using coins to model adding 5s and 10s

Unit 8 Math Focus Points

◆ Using cubes and the number line to show how addition combinations are related

◆ Representing the action of subtraction and addition situations using notation ($-, +, =$)

Whole Number Operations Understanding the properties of addition and subtraction

Unit 3 Math Focus Points

◆ Considering whether reordering three addends results in the same total

◆ Considering a generalization about reordering addends for all numbers

◆ Considering whether reordering the numbers in a subtraction problem results in the same total

◆ Considering the relationship between addition and subtraction

Whole Number Operations Adding even and odd numbers

Unit 8 Math Focus Points

◆ Characterizing even and odd numbers as those that do or do not make groups of two (partners) and two equal groups (teams)

◆ Investigating what happens with partners and teams when two groups are combined

◆ Finding combinations of odd and even numbers that make given numbers or determining that these combinations are not possible

◆ Making and testing conjectures about adding even and odd numbers

◆ Making and justifying generalizations about adding even and odd numbers

Computational Fluency Knowing addition combinations to 10 + 10

Unit 1 Math Focus Points

◆ Developing and achieving fluency with the make 10, +1, and +2 addition combinations

◆ Finding two addends that make 10

◆ Finding the missing addend to make a total of 10

◆ Doubling a quantity

◆ Developing fluency with the doubles combinations

Unit 2 Math Focus Points

◆ Reviewing known addition combinations (combinations of 10, +1, +2)

◆ Developing fluency with the doubles combinations to 10 + 10

◆ Achieving fluency with the doubles combinations

Unit 3 Math Focus Points

◆ Relating the doubles and near-doubles combinations

◆ Developing fluency with the near-doubles combinations

◆ Adding 10 to any number (or any number to 10)

◆ Developing fluency with the +10 combinations

◆ Achieving fluency with the near-doubles combinations

Unit 4 Math Focus Point

◆ Achieving fluency with the +10 combinations

Unit 8 Math Focus Points

◆ Relating unknown combinations to known combinations

◆ Developing and achieving fluency with the +9 and remaining combinations

The Base-Ten Number System Understanding the equivalence of one group and the discrete units that comprise it

Unit 1 Math Focus Points

◆ Identifying coins and their values

◆ Identifying how many pennies each coin is worth

◆ Identifying and using coin equivalencies

Unit 3 Math Focus Points

◆ Identifying coins and their values

◆ Identifying and using coin equivalencies

◆ Recognizing that the first digit of a 2-digit number designates the number of groups of 10 and the second digit designates the number of ones

◆ Solving problems about 10s and 1s

◆ Using a place-value model to represent a number as 10s and 1s

◆ Finding as many combinations of a number as possible, using only 10s and 1s

◆ Recognizing that different combinations of 10s and 1s for the same number are equivalent (e.g., 4 tens and 6 ones = 3 tens and 16 ones, etc.)

Unit 6 Math Focus Points

◆ Organizing cubes into 10s and 1s

◆ Using a place-value model to represent a number as 10s and 1s

◆ Using coin equivalencies

◆ Working with the relationship between 1, 10, and 100

Rational Numbers Understanding fractions as equal parts of a whole

Unit 7 Math Focus Points

- Finding equal parts of a whole and naming them with fractions, (e.g., $\frac{1}{2}$ is one of two equal parts; $\frac{1}{3}$ is one of three equal parts, and so on)
- Identifying and naming fractional parts that have numerators greater than 1 (e.g., $\frac{2}{3}$, $\frac{2}{4}$, $\frac{3}{4}$)
- Showing one half of an object
- Determining whether a block is half of another block
- Determining whether a region is half of a given rectangle
- Seeing different ways to make fourths of a square
- Recognizing the equivalence of different fourths of the same object
- Identifying halves, thirds, and fourths of regions

Rational Numbers Understanding fractions as equal parts of a group

Unit 7 Math Focus Points

- Finding equal parts of a group and naming them with fractions (e.g., $\frac{1}{2}$ is one of two equal parts; $\frac{1}{3}$ is one of three equal parts, and so on)
- Finding one half of a set
- Finding thirds and fourths of sets
- Finding fractions of sets
- Solving problems about finding halves of quantities in different contexts
- Solving problems that result in mixed numbers

Rational Numbers Using terms and notation

Unit 7 Math Focus Points

- Learning the term *one half* and the notation $\frac{1}{2}$
- Learning the term *one fourth* and the notation $\frac{1}{4}$
- Learning the term *one third* and the notation $\frac{1}{3}$
- Learning the terms and notation for fractions that contain more than one part (e.g., $\frac{2}{3}$, $\frac{2}{4}$, and $\frac{3}{4}$)
- Learning the terms and notation for mixed numbers (e.g., one and a half and $1\frac{1}{2}$)

GRADE 2

Patterns and Functions

Linear Relationships Describing and representing ratios

Unit 5 Math Focus Points

- Describing the relationship between two quantities in a constant ratio situation
- Using tables to represent the ratio relationship between two quantities
- Finding the value of one quantity in a constant ratio situation, given the value of the other

Using Tables and Graphs Using tables to represent change

Unit 5 Math Focus Points

◆ Connecting numbers in a table to the situation they represent

◆ Using conventional language for a table and its parts: rows, columns

◆ Describing the pattern in the numbers in a column and interpreting the pattern in terms of the situation the table represents

◆ Describing what is the same about situations that look different but can be represented by the same table

◆ Describing how the two numbers in the row of a table are connected to the situation the table represents

◆ Using information in a table to determine the relationship between two quantities

Number Sequences Constructing, describing, and extending number sequences with constant increments generated by various contexts

Unit 5 Math Focus Points

◆ Extending a repeating pattern

◆ Identifying the unit of a repeating pattern

◆ Creating a repeating pattern that has the same structure as, but different elements than, another repeating pattern (e.g., a red-blue pattern and a clap-tap head pattern)

◆ Defining even and odd numbers

◆ Determining and describing the number sequence associated with one of the elements in an AB, ABC, ABCD, or AABBC patterns (e.g., 2, 4, 6, 8, . . .; 3, 6, 9, . . .; 1, 4, 7, . . .)

◆ Determining the element of a repeating pattern associated with a particular counting number in AB, ABC, ABCD, or AABBC patterns (e.g., what color is the 8th element in a red-blue repeating pattern?)

◆ Determining how and why the same number sequence can be generated by different contexts

Data Analysis

Data Analysis Sorting and classifying data

Unit 4 Math Focus Points

◆ Grouping data into categories based on similar attributes

◆ Sorting a set of data by two attributes at one time

◆ Sorting the same set of data in different ways

Data Analysis Representing data

Unit 4 Math Focus Points

◆ Representing a set of data sorted into categories

◆ Using a Venn diagram to represent a sorted set of data

◆ Using equations to show how the sum of the responses in each category equals the total responses collected

◆ Comparing ways of organizing data

◆ Comparing representations of a set of data

◆ Ordering, representing, and describing a set of numerical data

◆ Representing data on a line plot

Data Analysis Describing data

Unit 1 Math Focus Points

◆ Making predictions about data

Unit 4 Math Focus Points

◆ Describing what the data show about the group surveyed

◆ Interpreting a data representation including a line plot

◆ Describing important features of a data set

◆ Describing a set of numerical data

◆ Comparing two sets of data

◆ Developing a hypothesis based on a set of data

Data Analysis Designing and carrying out a data investigation

Unit 1 Math Focus Points

◆ Collecting, counting, representing, discussing, interpreting, and comparing data

Unit 4 Math Focus Points

◆ Choosing a survey question
◆ Making a plan for collecting data
◆ Making predictions about data to be collected
◆ Collecting and recording data from a survey
◆ Interpreting and sharing results from a data investigation

GRADE 2

Geometry

Features of Shape Composing and decomposing 2-D and 3-D shapes

Unit 1 Math Focus Points

◆ Fitting shapes together to cover an area

Unit 2 Math Focus Points

◆ Combining shapes to make a new shape
◆ Covering a region, without gaps or overlaps, with a single shape or multiple shapes
◆ Covering a region, without gaps or overlaps, using different shapes
◆ Combining 3-D shapes to make a 3-D whole
◆ Drawing 3-D shapes

Features of Shape Describing, identifying, comparing, and sorting 2-D and 3-D shapes

Unit 2 Math Focus Points

◆ Describing attributes of and sorting 2-D shapes and 3-D shapes
◆ Identifying names and attributes of 2-D and 3-D shapes
◆ Attending to features of 3-D shapes, particularly the number and shape of faces
◆ Identifying categories for 2-D shapes
◆ Identifying a 3-D shape by touch
◆ Sorting polygons by the number of sides
◆ Sorting quadrilaterals by angle
◆ Identifying quadrilaterals as shapes with 4 sides
◆ Identifying rectangles as 4-sided shapes with 4 right angles
◆ Identifying important features of a rectangle
◆ Defining *biggest* in different ways
◆ Ordering rectangles from biggest to smallest
◆ Recognizing that rectangular prisms have rectangular faces
◆ Recognizing which faces of a rectangular prism are the same size and shape
◆ Constructing a rectangular prism from rectangles
◆ Visualizing and describing rectangular prisms
◆ Comparing rectangular prisms

Features of Shape Exploring mirror symmetry

Unit 2 Math Focus Points

◆ Describing and identifying objects and designs that have mirror symmetry
◆ Constructing 2-dimensional and 3-dimensional symmetrical designs with mirror symmetry
◆ Reflecting a shape across a line of symmetry

- Exploring symmetry by folding and cutting paper patterns
- Identifying lines of symmetry
- Orienting shapes so that a line of symmetry aligns with a mirror (*Shapes* software)
- Determining what makes a design symmetrical

GRADE 2

Measurement

Area Measurement **Visualizing the structure of arrays**

Unit 2 Math Focus Points

- Covering rectangles with arrays of tiles
- Arranging square tiles in rectangular arrays
- Constructing and describing rectangular arrays of tiles
- Making different rectangular arrays using the same number of tiles
- Drawing rectangles by attending to the lengths of the sides

Linear Measurement **Understanding length**

Unit 9 Math Focus Points

- Comparing two lengths
- Using direct and indirect comparison to identify equal lengths
- Identifying length and width as different dimensions of an object

Linear Measurement **Using linear units**

Unit 9 Math Focus Points

- Iterating units to measure length
- Estimating and calculating length using units that are related by a 2:1 ratio
- Identifying strategies for accurate measurement
- Considering sources of measurement error
- Understanding that different-sized units yield different counts (the smaller the unit, the higher the count)
- Establishing the need for and using a common unit in order to compare measurements
- Identifying and labeling partial units
- Recognizing that, given equal counts of two different units, the larger unit marks off a longer length

Linear Measurement **Measuring with standard units**

Unit 9 Math Focus Points

- Establishing the need for and using a standard unit of measure
- Creating and using a 12-inch measuring tool
- Iterating a 12-inch measuring tool
- Measuring lengths that are longer than 12 inches
- Using a ruler as a standard measuring tool
- Comparing a variety of measurement tools
- Becoming familiar with the terms *inches, feet, yards, centimeters* and *meters* as standard units of measure
- Using inches, feet, yards, centimeters, and meters to describe lengths
- Comparing centimeters and inches

Time **Representing time and calculating duration**

Unit 9 Math Focus Points

- Representing time as a horizontal sequence
- Connecting a time, its digital notation, and its representation on an analog clock to a timeline
- Naming and using notation for times that are 30 and 15 minutes before or after the hour
- Associating times with daily events
- Using a timeline to determine duration
- Moving forward and backward along a timeline in multiples of hours, half hours, and quarter hours
- Using a timeline to show a 24-hour period
- Recording events on a timeline

GRADE 2

Classroom Routines

How Many Pockets?

Units 2–3 and 5–9 Math Focus Points

- Making predictions about data
- Collecting, counting, representing, discussing, interpreting, and comparing data
- Counting by groups
- Counting a quantity in more than one way
- Using known combinations (i.e. combinations that make 10) to combine numbers
- Developing strategies for solving addition problems with many addends
- Using a place value model to represent a number as 10s and 1s
- Recognizing that the first digit of a 2-digit number designates the number of groups of 10 and the second digit designates the number of ones

- Identifying coins and their values
- Identifying and using coin equivalencies

Today's Number

Units 1–9 Math Focus Points

- Generating equivalent expressions for a number
- Developing fluency with addition and subtraction
- Using standard notation ($+, -, =$) to record expressions and write equations
- Using the number line and 100 chart to reason about the magnitude and relationship of numbers
- Skip counting by 2s, 5s, and 10s
- Identifying patterns in the multiples of 2, 5, and 10

Quick Images

Units 1–9 Math Focus Points

- Developing and analyzing visual images for quantities up to 10
- Developing fluency with the addition combinations to $10 + 10$
- Using known combinations (i.e. combinations that make 10) to combine numbers
- Recreating images of dots arranged in two by five arrays
- Using standard notation ($+, -, =$) to write equations
- Identifying names and attributes of 2-D shapes
- Using arrays and standard notation ($+, =$) to represent doubles to $10 + 10$
- Combining groups of tens and ones
- Adding or subtracting 10 to/from a two-digit number
- Noticing what happens to the tens place when a multiple of 10 is added or subtracted to/from a two-digit number
- Identifying coins and their values
- Adding coin amounts
- Using ratio relationships to solve problems
- Solving problems about an unknown change

What Time is It?

Units 1–9 Math Focus Points

- Using clocks as tools for keeping track of and measuring time
- Naming, notating, and telling time to the hour, half hour, and quarter hour on digital and analog clocks
- Associating times on the hour and half hour with daily events
- Determining what time it will be when given start and elapsed times that are multiples of 15 minutes
- Determining the number of minutes in hours, half hours, and quarter hours
- Counting by 5s
- Seeing a timeline as a representation of events over time
- Using a timeline to keep track of and compare time and events
- Determining the length of a given interval (e.g., 8:30 to 9:30) or activity (e.g., math class)
- Solving problems involving elapsed time

NCTM Curriculum Focal Points and Connections

The set of three curriculum focal points and related connections for mathematics in Grade 1 follow. These topics are the recommended content emphases for this grade level. It is essential that these focal points be addressed in contexts that promote problem solving, reasoning, communication, making connections, and designing and analyzing representations.

Grade 1 Curriculum Focal Points	Investigations Units
Number and Operations and *Algebra:* **Developing understandings of addition and subtraction and strategies for basic addition facts and related subtraction facts** Children develop strategies for adding and subtracting whole numbers on the basis of their earlier work with small numbers. They use a variety of models, including discrete objects, length-based models (e.g., lengths of connecting cubes), and number lines, to model "part-whole," "adding to," "taking away from," and "comparing" situations to develop an understanding of the meanings of addition and subtraction and strategies to solve such arithmetic problems. Children understand the connections between counting and the operations of addition and subtraction (e.g., adding two is the same as "counting on" two). They use properties of addition (commutativity and associativity) to add whole numbers, and they create and use increasingly sophisticated strategies based on these properties (e.g., "making tens") to solve addition and subtraction problems involving basic facts. By comparing a variety of solution strategies, children relate addition and subtraction as inverse operations.	**Addressed in the work of:** • *How Many of Each?* (Addition, Subtraction, and the Number System 1) • *Solving Story Problems* (Addition, Subtraction, and the Number System 2) • *Number Games and Crayon Puzzles* (Addition, Subtraction, and the Number System 3) • *Twos, Fives, and Tens* (Addition, Subtraction, and the Number System 4) • Classroom Routines: *Start With/Get To, Quick Images,* and *Tell a Story* **Also supported in the work of:** • *Fish Lengths and Animal Jumps* (Measurement) • *What Would You Rather Be?* (Data Analysis) • *Color, Shape, and Number Patterns* (Patterns and Functions) • Classroom Routine: *Quick Survey*
Number and Operations: **Developing an understanding of whole number relationships including grouping in tens and ones** Children compare and order whole numbers (at least to 100) to develop an understanding of and solve problems involving the relative sizes of these numbers. They think of whole numbers between 10 and 100 in terms of groups of tens and ones (especially recognizing the numbers 11 to 19 as 1 group of ten and particular numbers of ones). They understand the sequential order of the counting numbers and their relative magnitudes and represent numbers on a number line.	**Addressed in the work of:** • *How Many of Each?* (Addition, Subtraction, and the Number System 1) • *Solving Story Problems* (Addition, Subtraction, and the Number System 2) • *Number Games and Crayon Puzzles* (Addition, Subtraction, and the Number System 3) • *Twos, Fives, and Tens* (Addition, Subtraction, and the Number System 4) • Classroom Routines: *Start With/Get To, Quick Images,* and *Tell a Story*
Geometry: **Composing and decomposing geometric shapes** Children compose and decompose plane and solid figures (e.g., by putting two congruent isosceles triangles together to make a rhombus), thus building an understanding of part-whole relationships as well as the properties of the original and composite shapes. As they combine figures, they recognize them from different perspectives and orientations, describe their geometric attributes and properties, and determine how they are alike and different, in the process developing a background for measurement and initial understandings of such properties as congruence and symmetry.	**Addressed in the work of:** • *Making Shapes and Designing Quilts* (2-D Geometry) • *Blocks and Boxes* (3-D Geometry) • Technology: *Shapes* Software • Classroom Routine: *Quick Images*

Connections to the Focal Points	Investigations Units
Number and Operations and **Algebra:** Children use mathematical reasoning, including ideas such as commutativity and associativity and beginning ideas of tens and ones, to solve two-digit addition and subtraction problems with strategies that they understand and can explain. They solve both routine and nonroutine problems.	**Addressed in the work of:** • *How Many of Each?* (Addition, Subtraction, and the Number System 1) • *Solving Story Problems* (Addition, Subtraction, and the Number System 2) • *Number Games and Crayon Puzzles* (Addition, Subtraction, and the Number System 3) • *Twos, Fives, and Tens* (Addition, Subtraction, and the Number System 4) • Classroom Routine: *Tell a Story* **Also supported in the work of:** • *What Would You Rather Be?* (Data Analysis) • *Fish Lengths and Animal Jumps* (Measurement) • Classroom Routine: *Morning Meeting*
Measurement and **Data Analysis:** Children strengthen their sense of number by solving problems involving measurements and data. Measuring by laying multiple copies of a unit end to end and then counting the units by using groups of tens and ones supports children's understanding of number lines and number relationships. Representing measurements and discrete data in picture and bar graphs involves counting and comparisons that provide another meaningful connection to number relationships.	**Addressed in the work of:** • *What Would You Rather Be?* (Data Analysis) • *Fish Lengths and Animal Jumps* (Measurement) • Classroom Routine: *Quick Survey*
Algebra: Through identifying, describing, and applying number patterns and properties in developing strategies for basic facts, children learn about other properties of numbers and operations, such as odd and even (e.g., "Even numbers of objects can be paired, with none left over"), and 0 as the identity element for addition.	**Addressed in the work of:** • *Color, Shape, and Number Patterns* (Patterns and Functions) • Classroom Routine: *Morning Meeting* **Also supported in the work of:** • *Number Games and Crayon Puzzles* (Addition, Subtraction, and the Number System 3) • *Twos, Fives, and Tens* (Addition, Subtraction, and the Number System 4)

PART 9

Grade 1 Math Terms and Index

Each entry is identified by the Curriculum Unit number (in yellow) and its
page number(s).

B

Bar graphs. *See* Graphs.

Boxes

    collecting, U9: 10, 38, 43, 48

    constructing, U9: 10–11, 52–55, 57–58, 61, 111–112

    faces of, U9: 51–52

    relating size and shape to use, U9: 61–62, 118–119

Breaking numbers apart strategies, U3: 182–183, 186–187, 233, 234; U6: 153; U8: 16–17, 57, 110, 122–125

C

Calendar, U1: 13; U3: 142

Categorical data. *See* Data.

Categorizing

    by attributes, U4: 25–27, 29–32, 115–116

    pieces that don't fit in categories, U4: 12

    shapes, U4: 26–27

Cents, U1: 164

Changing numbers to make an easier problem strategy, U8: 57, 110, 122–125

Circles, U2: 26, 121

Classifying, U2: 122

    by attributes, U4: 10, 25–27, 29–32, 115–116

    shapes, U4: 26

Closed shapes, U2: 121

Codes, U7: 34–36, 38

Collecting data. *See* Data.

Combining problems. *See* Addition.

Commutative property of multiplication, U8: 62

Comparing

    blocks to pictures, U9: 35, 117

    boxes, U9: 58–59

    data, U4: 11, 81, 106, 123

    distances, U5: 64–66, 79–81, 85

    heights, U5: 42

    lengths, U5: 42–46, 50–51, 98

    numbers, U1: 61, 72–74, 78–79, 87, 103–106, 134–135

    repeating patterns, U7: 11, 16–17, 62–63, 66–67, 105–108, 142–145

    story problems, U5: 42–46, 50, 80–81, 84–85

    strategies for, U5: 51, 85–86, 90–91

    strategies for addition, U3: 127

    strategies for subtraction, U3: 199

    three-dimensional shapes, U9: 10, 25, 27–28, 31, 43, 46

Comparison problems

    of distances, U5: 63–66, 80–81, 84–85, 98

    of length, U5: 42–46, 50–51

    strategies for, U5: 51, 85–86, 90–91

Composing numbers. *See* Number composition.

Cones, U9: 107

Constant rate of increase. *See* Rate of increase.

Contexts, U3: 133–134; U5: 35, 91

Corners. *See* Vertices.

Counting, U8: 30

    by 1s, U3: 148–149; U8: 10, 27–31, 36, 41, 45, 55, 67–69, 107–108, 110–115, 117–119, 121, 137, 140–141, 168–169

    by 4s, U8: 67–69, 78–79, 81, 86

    to 5, U8: 11, 72–74, 78–79, 81, 86

    by 5s, U8: 72–74, 81

    to 10, U8: 10, 16–17, 27–31, 36, 41, 45, 97–98, 100–101, 110–115, 117, 121–125, 168–169

    by 10s, U8: 11, 12, 107–108, 110–115, 117–119, 121, 168–169

    to 20, U1: 10, 44, 45, 57–59, 62, 67, 85–87

    to 60, U3: 148–149; U8: 10, 27–31, 36, 41, 45

    to 100, U3: 160–162, 171

    adding doubles, U8: 137

    backward, U1: 78

    combination of groups and ones, U8: 137–138

    common errors, U8: 44–45, 159–160

    connecting numbers and quantities, U3: 205

    conservation, U1: 194; U3: 205; U8: 131

    forward and backward, U1: 10, 13, 74–76; U3: 31

    by groups, U1: 194; U3: 205, 234; U7: 12, 75–79, 83–85, 87, 89–91, 102, 105; U8: 132, 137–138, 141–142

    higher numbers in sequence, U3: 165

    larger numbers, U3: 141–149

    on number lines, U3: 162, 166, 171

    numbers to quantities, U1: 194–195; U8: 131, 133

    observing students during, U3: 206

    one-to-one correspondence, U1: 194; U3: 205; U8: 131

    orally, U1: 195; U3: 206; U8: 133

    quantities, U1: 62–63

    by rote, U1: 194; U3: 205; U8: 38–39, 131

    skills and concepts of, U3: 10–12, 205

    strategies for

        counting all, U3: 127, 189

        counting back, U3: 186, 189

        counting on, U3: 41–42, 59–62, 65–67, 189, 226

        double-checking, U1: 59

        grouping counters, U1: 58–59

        organizing objects, U3: 205; U8: 30, 76–77, 85, 140–142, 164–165

        touching as you count, U1: 58

    two-to-one relationship, U8: 11, 55–58, 61–64, 66–69, 78–79, 81–83, 85–86, 161, 162–163

    by writing numbers, U1: 195; U3: 151–154, 156, 160–162, 169, 206; U8: 38–39, 41–42, 44–45, 133, 159–160

Counting all strategy, U1: 118–120, 131, 137, 142–143, 203–204, 213, 218–219, 234–236; U3: 71–72, 97, 100, 127, 181–182, 189–191, 224; U6: 11–12, 54, 59, 112, 128–130, 134, 160, 189–191; U8: 30, 57–58, 67–69, 140–141, 162–163

Counting and adjusting numbers strategy, U1: 213

H

Height, U5: 42
Heptagons, U2: 121
Hexagonal prisms, U9: 107
Hexagons, U7: 99; U9: 10–11
    composing/decomposing,
        U2: 32–34, 40, 46–47, 143–144
    describing, U2: 31–32
    identification of, U2: 121
***How Many of Each?* problems**
    about more, U6: 77–79, 90–93, 97,
        151–152, 181
    common difficulties with,
        U1: 215–216
    finding all combinations,
        U1: 151–155, 174–178, 213–214,
        236–237; U3: 13, 16, 32–36,
        218–219
    recording, U1: 214
    strategies for recording, U1: 214
    strategies for solving, U1: 213–214;
        U3: 179–180, 187, 234;
        U6: 149–150, 154
    zero as an addend in, U6: 177–178

I

Inequalities, U3: 113–118, 120–121, 125
Interpreting data. *See* Data.
Intervention, U1: 22

J

"Just know" strategy, U1: 204, 207,
    220, 234–236; U6: 54, 59, 191;
    U8: 110, 162

K

Known combinations strategy,
    U1: 118–120, 131, 137, 142–143,
    204, 214, 220, 234–235;
    U3: 179–180, 187, 200, 224, 227,
    229, 232; U5: 90; U6: 11, 54, 59, 87,
    125, 134, 154, 161–162, 164, 167,
    189–192; U8: 55, 57–58, 110

L

Length
    comparison of, U5: 42–46, 50–51, 87
    developing and understanding of,
        U5: 10
    measurement of, U5: 23–27, 35–47,
        50, 87–88
Less than sign (<), U1: 91–92, 103–104;
    U3: 12, 113, 120, 125; U8: 110–111,
    117, 121

M

Measurement, U3: 13
    accuracy of, U5: 32–33, 35–40,
        55–56, 92
    of area, U3: 141–149, 157–158
    common mistakes, U5: 35–37
    comparing, U5: 42–46, 50–51, 63–66
    contexts, U5: 35
    with different units, U5: 29–34,
        63–67, 69–72, 74–77, 84–85,
        95–96, 100
    of distances, U5: 63–66, 69–72, 74–77
    of length, U5: 23–27, 29–31, 35–47,
        50, 53–55
    with partial units, U5: 24, 26–27, 30,
        32, 64, 74, 89, 97, 99
    with same units, U5: 23–27, 85, 93–94
    start and end points, U5: 24, 29–30,
        32, 36, 92
    understanding length, U5: 10
    using linear units, U5: 10–11
Minus sign (−), U3: 93–94, 101, 239
Missing parts, U3: 37–42, 44–45, 76,
    122, 126, 132, 199
Money, U1: 164
Multiplication, U1: 28
    commutative property of, U8: 62

N

Nonagons, U2: 121
Non-polygons, U2: 26, 121
Notation
    for addition, U1: 119, 131, 161–162,
        200–201; U3: 72, 127, 184–185;
        U6: 12, 28, 143; U8: 17, 97–99,
        118, 121
    assessment of use of, U3: 198

    equal sign (=), U3: 76–77; U6: 29,
        145–146
    for inequalities, U3: 113
    for ordering numbers, U1: 91–93
    representation of mathematical
        thinking by, U3: 12–13
    representing strategies for addition,
        U1: 13
    for subtraction, U3: 12, 93–94, 101,
        239; U6: 12, 137, 144
Number composition, U1: 11–12,
    151–155, 157–162, 164–166,
    174–178; U3: 10–11, 113–118,
    120–121, 125–126, 233–234
Number line, U1: 13; U6: 11, 18, 59, 130
    counting forward and backward on,
        U3: 31, 140
    counting larger numbers, U3: 142
    counting to one hundred, U3: 162,
        166, 171
    as representations of number
        system, U3: 160
    for subtraction problems, U3: 101
Number relationships strategy,
    U3: 97, 100–101, 127; U6: 11, 125,
    129–130, 133, 137, 161–162
Numbers. *See also* Number
    composition; Number sequences.
    U6: 10–11
    breaking apart, U1: 170–173
    comparing, U1: 61, 72–74, 78–79, 87,
        103–106, 112, 134–135
    connecting names and symbols to
        quantities, U1: 10
    connecting names and written form
        to quantities, U1: 122–124
    connecting to quantities, U3: 205
    conservation, U3: 205
    ordering, U1: 89–93
    reading, U8: 44–45
    as representation of data, U4: 44, 121

representing counting strategies, U8: 57

teens, U3: 165

two-digit, U8: 110–115, 117–119, 168–169

writing, U3: 152–153; U8: 38–39, 41–42, 44–45, 159–160

Number sequences, U7: 127–128, 146–149

association with repeating patterns, U7: 11–12, 75–79, 81, 87–91, 98–108, 101–102, 105

counting by twos, U7: 89–91

extending with constant increments, U7: 12, 16–17

generation of with various story contexts, U7: 105–108

Number system, U3: 160

Numerical data. *See* Data.

Numerical reasoning, U3: 190–191; U6: 161–162

O

Octagonal prism, U9: 107

Octagons, U2: 121

Octahedron, U9: 107

Odd numbers, U7: 79, 94

One, U1: 17–18

Ordering, U1: 67

data, U4: 12

numbers, U1: 89–93

quantities, U1: 62–63

Organization strategy, U8: 30, 76–77, 85, 140–142, 164–165

Organizing data. *See* Data.

Ovals, U2: 121

P

Parallelograms. *See also* Quadrilaterals; Rectangles; Rhombuses; Squares. U2: 122

Patterns. *See also* Repeating patterns. determining if it repeats, U7: 46–47

Pennies, U1: 164

Pentagonal pyramid, U9: 107

Pentagons, U2: 121

Plus sign (+), U1: 110, 119, 131, 161–162, 200; U3: 72, 127, 184

Points. *See* Vertices.

Polygons. *See also specific polygon.* U2: 79, 121

angles of, U2: 92, 122

attributes, U2: 26, 78–79, 132

closed shapes, U2: 121

equilateral, U2: 79, 121

regular, U2: 121

simple, U2: 121

Polyhedra. *See also* Geoblocks; Three-dimensional shapes; *specific polyhedron.*

Prediction

of color of numbered item in a repeating pattern, U7: 40–44, 55, 58–60, 64

of next item in a repeating pattern, U7: 10, 27–28, 37, 64, 93, 117–118, 138

shape of specific item in numbered sequence, U7: 93–96, 98–99, 104

Prisms, U9: 107

Proofs, U6: 149

Properties

associative property of addition, U8: 16–17

commutative property of addition, U6: 37–38

commutative property of multiplication, U8: 62

Pyramids, U9: 107

Q

Quadrilaterals. *See also* Parallelograms; Rectangles; Squares.

attributes of, U2: 86–87

classifications of, U2: 122

compared to triangles, U2: 91–92

creating on dot paper, U2: 88, 94, 100

identification of, U2: 121

R

Rate of increase

adding two, U7: 89–91

constant with a starting amount, U7: 75–79, 81, 88–91, 101, 105, 146–147

Rectangles. *See also* Squares. U2: 26, 86–87, 122

Rectangular prisms, U9: 10

attributes of, U9: 51–52, 107–108

comparing, U9: 58–59

constructing boxes, U9: 10–11, 52–55, 57–58, 61, 111–112

constructing of other three-dimensional shapes, U9: 11, 30–31, 42–43, 46

Regular shapes, U2: 121

Related problems, U3: 188; U6: 43, 110, 115; U8: 107

Repeated addition strategy, U8: 57–58

Repeating patterns

associated with number sequences, U7: 11–12, 98–99, 118, 148–149

body movement patterns, U7: 33–38, 41, 50–51, 99, 139

comparing, U7: 62–63, 66–67, 142–145

constructing, U7: 10, 29–31, 33–38, 49–51, 53–54, 59, 64

describing, U7: 10, 27–28, 30–31, 33, 37, 55, 58–60, 64, 117–118, 138

extending, U7: 10, 27–28, 37

of first graders, U7: 119–120

five-to-one relationship, U8: 72–74

identifying the units of, U7: 10–11, 47–51, 55, 59, 64, 93, 117, 140–141

making code for, U7: 34–36, 38

predicting specific value in numbered sequence, U7: 37, 40–44, 55, 58–60, 64, 93–96, 104, 117–118, 138

of shapes, U7: 93–96, 104

two-to-one relationship, U8: 61–64

units of, U7: 53–54, 59, 64

Representations, U1: 67, 214

of addition solutions, U8: 76

of body movement patterns, U7: 33–34

of categorical data, U4: 10, 30–32, 44–45, 56–59, 63, 76–79, 82, 91, 111, 119–120

drawings of three-dimensional shapes, U9: 69–73, 75–77, 82, 113–114, 120–121

equations, U6: 27–29, 31, 47, 165, 176–177, 182, 193–194